RICHARD A. FOSCHINO

MOUNTAIN REVENGE

To Nathaniel, Enjoy! Foschino '03

Mountain Top Publishing
Briceville, Tennessee

ABOUT THE AUTHOR

Richard Foschino was born in New York City in 1947 and grew up in the Catskill Mountains of New York State. In 1975 he began a law enforcement career that would span more than twenty-five years.

In 1979 he moved his wife and two children from New York to Tennessee, settling in a small town about twenty-five miles north of Knoxville. He joined the sheriff's department and through the years rose to the rank of Chief Deputy.

The greatest challenge of his career was the assignment of a series of unsolved murders that occurred in remote areas of the county years ago. Writing this book gives him the opportunity to share the excitement, disappointments, human emotions, and personal satisfaction he experienced when he met the challenges posed by these cold case files.

Mountain Revenge is his way of writing one of these true stories in a form other than a police report.

Published by
Mountain Top Publishing
P.O. Box 218
Briceville, Tennessee 37710

© 2003 by Richard A. Foschino
All Rights Reserved

First printing 2003

Library of Congress Catalog Card Number: 97-70710

ISBN 0-9724215-0-5

Printed in the United States of America

CONTENTS

CONTENTS

To Julia

This is a true story. All major events documented within these pages were based on fact. Many of the names have been changed as no real purpose would be served by revealing true identities. Any relation to real persons whose names were used as characters in this book is strictly a coincidence.

Richard Foschino is portrayed as Lieutenant Anthony Callo.

PREFACE

Imagine if you will, or perhaps you don't have to imagine, that a loved one, relative, or close friend has been the victim of a brutal homicide.

The United States Department of Justice, Federal Bureau of Investigation's report on crime in the United States, released in August 2000 states that the average national solve rate for the crime of murder is sixty-nine percent. The remaining thirty-one percent represents unsolved murders that will affect many thousands of people across this country. They will never have closure to their case. It also means that there is a dangerous segment of our society that will never be prosecuted for their crime and will be free to perhaps kill again.

After working for months, or even years, the police are unable to solve the case and bring those responsible to justice. Leads in the investigation have stopped coming in and the investigators are frustrated with the lack of progress in the case. You want some answers and are entitled to them. Someone is responsible for this terrible crime.

You may have a suspect in mind and find it hard to understand why the police can't make an arrest. The thought of even taking matters into your own hands has crossed your mind, but you think better of that idea. Two wrongs don't make a right.

The police may have a suspect in mind also, but they must gather enough evidence to make it stick. After a lengthy investigation, an arrest, and a trial, an acquittal would be devastating.

With the lack of progress in the investigation the police may simply have to put the case on the "back burner" and move on to other matters. However, there is still a glimmer of hope. Although the case may not be solved, it will never be closed. There is no statute of limitations on the crime of murder.

Many documented cases exist where new evidence surfaced, some times many years later, or new technology gave the police the tools they needed to re-examine an old case and put into place the missing pieces of the puzzle needed to bring the case to a successful conclusion.

In the case described in this book for years the unfortunate facts were that greed and corruption took priority, and seemed more important to those in power than the feelings and emotional stress of the murder victim's loved ones.

Thank God there came along a man who was deeply concerned, honest, and dedicated enough to do what it took to learn the truth. A man who had compassion and refused to give up until the truth was known by all.

Chapter 1

The Teeth Have Fillings

August 20, 1980 was a typically hot mid-summer day. One of those East Tennessee days when the humidity was higher than the temperature and it seemed you could cut the air with a knife.

Virgil Perkins was staying close to the air conditioner of his small, wood frame home on Frost Bottom Road. The "bottom" as it was called was located in the westernmost corner of the county. He was out early this morning, preparing his boat for a night of fishing to begin around 10:00 p.m. His plan called for getting out again only after the sun went down and the smothering heat subsided.

He knew the fish wouldn't be biting, but Virgil loved the outdoors since he was a boy and received a satisfaction he couldn't put into words from being one with nature.

He wasn't a man who could be forced to stay indoors for too long a time.

Virgil's wife Martha, a petite, silver-haired, country woman in her mid sixties, was concerned about her husband's health since he suffered a minor stroke last year. She didn't like him going to the lake or into the woods alone and worried whenever he planned one of his outings. She felt more at ease when he planned to take along one of his buddies. Because the doctor's orders were for him not to spend too much time out in the heat of the day, she didn't mind when he was out most of the night fishing. She wasn't jealous of mother nature.

Virgil was sitting comfortably in his favorite chair in the living room, sipping a cold glass of iced tea, when movement in the front yard caught his eye. He got up and went to the large picture window. His dog, Mutt, was attracted to and preoccupied with something in the grass. He figured it must be something special to the old mutt, because all he ever did on a hot and humid day like this is find a comfortable place in the shade to lay down.

"Hey, Martha," he called to his wife, who was in the kitchen cleaning up the dishes from lunch. "Come here and look at this crazy old dog. He must have gotten hold of a snake or something."

"Wouldn't surprise me none. This heat has really brought them snakes out the last week or so," she said as she joined her husband at the

14

window. "They must be comin' out of the mountains lookin' for water."

"That dog just ain't actin' right," said Virgil as he headed out to take a look.

When he got into the yard, Virgil called to his dog. The dog acted as if his master wasn't even there. He walked slowly over to where the dog was in the yard. He rarely got in a hurry to anything. As he approached, he was surprised that the dog didn't obey his commands. He had to yell. "Get away. Go lay down somewhere!"

"LORD GOD!" he gasped as he leaned over and realized what he encountered was not a snake after all. It was a bone. A human jaw bone.

When he jerked away, Martha sensed something was wrong and came out onto the front porch.

"Hell fire, Martha, call the law. It's a damn jaw bone. A person's jaw bone." Martha knew he was upset because they were both regular church going and God fearing people, and the only time she ever heard him use profanity was when he was extremely upset or excited.

Martha ran inside and awkwardly dialed the sheriff's department. She was excited as well and was breathing heavily into the phone. She explained to the dispatcher about her husbands discovery and gave her directions to the Perkins home. The dispatcher assured her a deputy would be there shortly.

"They're on the way, Virgil," she told him when she came back out onto the porch. "She said

15

not to touch or move anything."

While they waited, Virgil began to speculate.

"Bet it's one of them convicts that escaped from Brushy Mountain back in the spring," he told his wife.

Brushy Mountain State Penitentiary was on the other side of the mountain, tucked into the side of Graves Gap like a King's castle.

The rugged terrain served as the moat, discouraging all but the most determined inmates from trying their luck at freedom. James Earl Ray, convicted of the assassination of Doctor Martin Luther King Jr. in 1968 in Memphis, tried unsuccessfully to escape some time ago. The rugged mountains, deep valleys, and rattle-snake infested rock ledges proved to be too much for him to overcome. It was unlikely anyone made it this far on foot.

Meanwhile, the Sheriff Department's dispatcher radioed to a patrol unit the nature of the call and he was rushing to the scene. Knowing the bottom was at least twenty minutes away from his location, the deputy decided to take Dutch Valley Road. Although the road was winding, it was the shortest route to the bottom.

By the time the deputy arrived, several people had gathered in Virgil's yard. Nearly everyone in the bottom had a police scanner. Suddenly the terrible heat of the afternoon didn't seem to bother anyone; not even Virgil. This was the most excitement in the bottom since a year ago

16

when a drunk staggered out into the road and was run over by a cattle truck.

"Hi, I'm Virgil Perkins. This here's my place. My wife's the one who called," Virgil told the deputy even before he got out of his patrol car.

"How you doin,' Mr. Perkins? What have we got here?"

"Well, I noticed my old dog, that's him chained there by the porch. I noticed him carrying on in the yard. At first I thought it was a snake. They're bad here this time of year. Specially since it's been so dry. Anyway, I took a closer look and seen it was a man's jaw bone. Well, I say a man's jaw bone. For all I know it could be a woman's. But I do know it's a person's 'cause it's got teeth with fillin's in them." Virgil felt more confident since some of his neighbors agreed with him after they took a look at it.

They both started over to the middle of the yard to where the dog had abandoned the bone.

"Jesus! That's what it is all right," the deputy said as he reached down and picked it up. They both got a whiff of the unmistakable stench of decaying flesh.

"You know, now that I think about it, I was sittin' out on the porch a while back and the wind musta picked up on something dead. I just thought it was a road kill somewhere close by," Virgil said as the smell jarred his memory.

"Well, I'm sure it's human," the deputy said as he glanced over the yard hoping to see more bones. "I better get a detective down here."

17

He placed the bone carefully in the grass. Going back to his patrol car, he called dispatch to ask for a detective.

Captain John Miller had been with the sheriff's department about a year. He had a law enforcement background and served with several other agencies, including the Oak Ridge Police Department. He knew his way around the system and he knew how to get things done. Miller had been successful lately with a couple of complex investigations. One case involved a large scale burglary ring and another a stolen car and chop shop operation. His success made the sheriff look good, and that meant votes.

During the trip to the scene, he tried to recall any missing persons reports in his jurisdiction. Then he remembered, as did Virgil Perkins, the three escaped convicts from Brushy Mountain. As far as he knew they had not yet been located.

By the time Miller arrived at the scene there were cars lined along both sides of the roadway in front of the Perkins home. The scene was not hard to find. He wasn't surprised. He knew how fast news spread in the bottom; especially bad news. He hoped the deputy had taken precautions to protect the scene and was pleased when he got out of his car, spotting the yellow crime scene tape strung from tree to tree across the yard.

Miller examined the bone carefully and was glad to see there were some teeth in it. The fact that the teeth had fillings might make identification easier. He made himself a note to check with the prison to see if the dental records of the convicts were there or in the main prison in Nashville.

"Where do you start on something like this?" the deputy asked.

"I know where I'm going to start, Paul. I'm going to call Doctor Bass at the university."

Miller never worked a case with Doctor Bass, but attended several training classes for police officers that Bass instructed. In fact he was at a four-hour seminar a week before in Knoxville.

The deputy looked puzzled. "Is he the medical examiner or something?"

"No. He's a professor of anthropology at U. T. He's also the state forensic anthropologist. You wouldn't believe what Bill Bass can tell you from a pile of bones. He's one of the best in the country," Miller explained. "I'm going to put this in a paper bag and mark it. Then I'm going to look around a little. Whew...it can't be too old. It still stinks like hell." He marked his evidence and put it in the trunk of his car. Not locating any more bones in the immediate area he gave up his search.

Calling from the Perkins phone, he was glad when the secretary told him Doctor Bass was not in a class. When Doctor Bass picked up the phone, Miller explained the details of the bone's discovery.

Miller explained to Mr. and Mrs. Perkins who Doctor Bass was and told them they would be back in the morning. He told them there would be a deputy there all night to safeguard the scene. Virgil knew there would be no way he would be going fishing tonight.

Miller drove back to the office. He wanted to fill the sheriff in on what they had found. He also planned to tell the sheriff he thought it would be best to keep this as quiet as they could for now. He really didn't want to deal with the press yet. As things stood now, there would be more questions than he had answers for.

The next morning Doctor Bass arrived at the sheriff's office with several of his graduate students right on time. They examined the mandible carefully and told Miller it was in good condition. The inspection was brief, and Miller was surprised by the amount of information they provided.

Doctor Bass determined the mandible contained six teeth. Three of them contained fillings. He also said it was that of an adult white male, not under the age of twenty, and probably much older. His thoughts were that the individual had been dead from three months to a year. He added that the body had never been buried.

When they arrived at the scene, Miller stood aside allowing Doctor Bass and his students to do their thing. After about two hours they recovered a number of additional bone fragments from the yard. However, the search was hampered by the heavy underbrush and they decided if there wasn't an identification made by fall they would return to look for more evidence.

"What do you think, Doctor Bass?" Miller asked.

"We've got some animal bones mixed in,

but some of these fragments are human. What I'll have to do is go back to the university and conduct some tests. I can have a report for you in a couple of days."

"I think you should know there were three convicts escaped from the prison a while back that haven't been located yet," Miller told him.

"Yes sir. Brushy Mountain is just over a couple of those ridges. I had a deputy go by there last night and pick up a copy of their dental records. I thought you could compare them to the dental work this guy had done."

"Oh, by the way. We also found a large portion of what appears to be a light colored short-sleeved shirt, a pull-over type. It also has a strong odor of decay. I think it might have been worn by the victim at the time of death. I'll preserve it too."

Doctor Bass gathered his material and headed back to Knoxville. Miller stayed behind to check with some of the people living in the area. Several told him they smelled a strong foul odor in the area about a month ago, but it went away.

As he drove back to the office, he was confident that some day more remains of this poor soul would be discovered and perhaps tell the rest of the story. He knew somewhere in the nearby woods was what was left of some guy that once was a walking, talking human being.

He thought surely this man had a wife or someone who was aware that he was missing. Why then was there no missing person report? He also wondered how he died. He had a feeling in the pit of his stomach that some day there would be an investigation into this man's death, and he knew it was going to be a homicide investigation.

Chapter 2

The Missing Person

Oak Ridge is a city with a population of about 30,000 people, with most of the employed population working at the plants. Plants with names such as Y-12, X-10, and K-25, so-named because in 1942 the city was selected as the headquarters for the United States wartime atomic energy program, known as the Manhattan Project.

The city was built by the U.S. Army Corps of Engineers behind security fences. As a wartime boomtown, its population reached 75,000. In the early fifties the fences came down and the area was opened for private construction, and in 1959 the community voted to incorporate as a city.

In1980 the city had the most well-equipped and up to date police department in the county.

On September 2, 1980, the Oak Ridge Police Department received a call from a store owner in a small shopping center in the middle of town. The caller was complaining about a car parked in one of the store's spaces for the last couple of months, which appeared to be abandoned.

Patrolman Mayes remembered seeing the car often during his patrol shifts, when he was dispatched to the location in Grove Center. Arriving at the car, he noticed all four tires were low on air pressure; an indication the vehicle had been parked there for some time. He called the license plate number into his dispatcher and learned the vehicle was registered to Jack Keller, with an address on Holston Lane in Oak Ridge. The vehicle was a 1973 Oldsmobile 98.

Mayes found all the doors locked, and tagged the vehicle with an abandoned vehicle sticker. At the end of his shift he wrote a brief report. No other action was taken. He did decide during his next shift, if he had time, he would check the Holston Lane address to see if he could locate Mr. Keller.

A week after the abandoned vehicle was reported to the police, a slender, good looking, female about twenty-five years old walked into the police station asking to see an officer.

Captain Graves approached her and asked if he could help.

"Yes, my name is Brenda Baker. I wanted to report a friend missing. I just drove through Grove Center and saw his car, and I noticed all his tires were flat and it had a red police sticker on the window."

"What's his name?"

"His name is Jack Keller. He lives on Holston Lane but I haven't seen him around since the end of June."

Just as Brenda told the Captain Jack's name, Officer Mayes walked into the hallway and overheard her.

"Did you say Jack Keller?" Mayes asked.

"Yes. Do you know him?"

"No, I don't know him but I checked a car in Grove Center about a week ago that's registered to him. I've been meaning to check his address and tell him he needs to move his car. I just haven't had a chance."

"How old is Jack, Miss Baker?" Captain Graves asked.

"He's in his mid-thirties."

"Come into my office and I'll get the information from you."

"Sure. I have his mother's telephone number, but I wasn't sure if I should call her yet. I didn't want her to worry."

Brenda gave Graves the information including a description that Jack was about five feet nine inches tall, weighed about one hundred-sixty pounds, had brown hair and blue gray eyes. She said he was from Wisconsin but had lived in Oak Ridge about four years. She also said he was self-employed as a sign painter, and played the drums in a local band.

Graves wrote a missing person report but decided because Jack was an adult, he would contact his mother before he initiated an investigation.

"Oh yeah, one more thing I just remembered," Brenda said as she got up to leave. "Jack told me the last time I saw him that he was being evicted from his apartment because he stored paint there. His landlord said he was smelling up the place."

After Brenda left, he dialed the number she gave him for Jack's mother in Wisconsin.

"Mrs. Keller, this is Captain Graves with the police department in Oak Ridge, Tennessee. I'm calling you because a woman came into the station today concerned about not having seen your son Jack in the last few months. I'm just trying to locate him and make sure he's okay."

"Oh my, I haven't seen Jack since he left here in June. He was here for a visit and left on June twenty-third. As far as I knew he was going back to Tennessee. He moves around a lot, but he always keeps in touch with us," she said.

Graves asked Mrs. Keller for a recent photograph of her son. He didn't want her to know he was beginning to become concerned himself. He didn't tell her about Jack's car being abandoned for the last couple of months.

Graves called the detective division. "Hey Louis, come around to my office. I've got something I want you to look into."

"What's up, Captain?"

"I took a missing person report a few minutes ago. This guy's name is Jack Keller. Sound familiar to you?"

"Jack Keller. Yeah. I think we arrested him a couple of times. Public drunk I think. Nothing serious."

"Anyway, I just got off the phone with his mother in Wisconsin. She says she hasn't heard from him since June. She says that's pretty unusual. And Mayes tagged his car about a week ago over in Grove Center. He said it looked like it's been there a long time."

"I'll see what I can do with it," Louis said.

"Here's the file. Shit, everybody's got to be somewhere, Louis. And I know if anybody can find him, you can," Graves said with a big smile.

"Gee thanks, Captain. I guess the first place to look would be the county jail. Who knows, maybe he don't want to be found."

Louis Landau had been with the department for more than ten years. Anyone familiar with him knew he had his finger on the pulse of crime in the city. He knew the entire criminal element and over the years had developed a long list of snitches and informants. He was well-liked by the other officers and respected for his abilities by other departments. He was a big man, but his size didn't intimidate anyone because he was very soft spoken. He attended church regularly and rarely used profanity, something unusual for a police officer.

Louis went back to his office with the case file Captain Graves had started and read over the report. A call to the county jail revealed there was no report of Jack Keller being in jail presently or during the last few months. He then called the wrecker service and had Keller's car towed to the department impound lot.

He opened the car with a slim jim; a tool used to slip down into the door along the window. Once inside the car, he noticed it appeared that all this guy owned in this world was in there. Louis got the feeling Keller was moving or had been living out of his car. He also noticed the clothing had an odor of mildew.

The next morning Landau drove over to the Holston Lane address to check Keller's apartment. He spoke with some of the tenants and learned Jack had not been there since June or July. Most of his old neighbors were glad he was gone because his sign painting smelled up the entire building. He got the phone number of the landlord and headed back to the office to make some calls. The day was gloomy, and it was starting to rain. He decided to do as much as he could by phone and put off the leg work for a nicer day.

As it turned out, Landau knew the landlord. He had dealings with him about some of his other tenants in the past. He always found him to be pleasant and very cooperative.

"Arvil, this is Louis Landau at the police department. How are you today?"

"Well, to tell you the truth Louis, this rain has got my arthritis actin' up. That aside, I guess I'm doin' okay. I woke up this morning."

Landau knew even if the sun was shining and it was a beautiful day, Arvil would have something to complain about.

"Hey Arvil, the reason I'm calling is I'm checking on one of your tenants. A guy named Jack Keller."

"You mean one of my former tenants Louis. I threw him out; had him evicted a couple of months ago. This guy, all he ever did is drink and smell up the place with his paints. I told him a dozen times, he couldn't paint signs in the apartment. Finally I had enough and told him to get out."

"Yeah, that's what some of the other tenants told me. Do you have any idea where he moved to, Arvil?"

"No, I sure don't. He's probably shackin' with one of his girlfriends. He had enough of them."

"Pretty popular with the women, was he?"

"He sure was. Seemed like he had a new one every week. And it seemed like they got younger and younger too. One of my tenants told me they seen him goin' in with some that they knew couldn't have been a day over fifteen. Shit, Louis, they even seen a black girl go in with him sometimes. What do ya think of that? I'll tell you what's the truth, I'm glad he's gone."

Arvil liked to talk and Louis liked to listen; and it was paying off. He wasn't finding out where Keller was, but he was getting some interesting information about him.

"Is he in some kinda trouble Louis?"

"No. He's not in any trouble with the law. He hasn't been seen for a while and some of his friends and family are getting a little concerned. I'm just trying to find him, that's all."

"Well, it wouldn't surprise me none if he was," Arvil said. "I think he's one of them what you call dopers. He had some kind of a band and you know that's what them kind do, Louis."

"Is there anything else you can tell me that might help, Arvil?"

"Yeah, he told me the last time I seen him that he was having his mail forwarded to a friend of his down in River City. A guy named Danny Litton, I think he said. Oh yeah, he had one of those storage places over at Elza Gate Storage. He told me once that's where he stored his drums. It's a damn good thing he didn't keep them here is all I can say. That would have been all I needed. The paint, and the drums, and everybody would have been movin' out on me," Arvil started laughing. "Could you imagine that Louis?"

A call to Elza Gate Storage confirmed Keller had a space rented but hadn't been seen there for a time either.

The lead picked up from Arvil about his friend in River City was interesting. Louis made a call to the only Danny Litton in the phone book; there was no answer.

Taking a break he walked down to the officer's break room for a cup of coffee where he asked some of the officers if they knew Keller. Several of them were familiar with him and knew him to be a heavy drinker and a ladies man. They also recalled him being arrested a couple of times. When he got back to the office, Louis tried calling Danny Litton again. This time there was an answer.

"Is this Danny Litton?"

"Yeah. Who's this?"

"Danny, this is Detective Landau with the Oak Ridge Police Department. I'm calling because I'm trying to locate a guy by the name Jack Keller. I understand he's a friend of yours."

"Yeah, Jack's a friend of mine. What's going on with him? Is he in trouble with the law? Is he okay? Jesus Christ, what's he into now?"

"Slow down a minute, buddy," Landau said. "I'm just trying to locate him. He's not in any trouble. It's just that someone came into the station and reported him missing. Said they hadn't seen him in a couple of months," Louis explained.

"I'm sorry for asking so many questions. It's just that Jack's a real good friend and I haven't seen him or heard from him in months."

"I understand he had his mail forwarded to you?"

"Yeah. He had to move and wanted me to get his mail until he found another place."

"Danny, if you're going to be home for a while, I'd like to come down and talk to you and go over his mail. I can leave the station in a few minutes. That okay with you?"

"Yeah, sure, I'll be here."

When Landau arrived at Litton's house he

had his mail ready for him. Most of it was unimportant, but there was a statement from an Oak Ridge bank. He opened it and noticed the last transaction of any kind was a withdrawal of a hundred dollars on July 8th, after a deposit made on July 7th. There was a balance of ten dollars in the account.

Louis got the names of a couple more of Jack's friends from Danny Litton, who said he had been checking with everyone who knew Jack. None of them knew of his whereabouts.

When Louis left Litton's house, he couldn't help the funny feeling he had about him. Litton seemed really concerned about Jack, but he also seemed to be a little nervous. There was something Litton was not telling him.

Back at the sheriff's office, Captain John Miller was going over the report he just received form Doctor Bass. The comparison of the dental records of the escaped convicts with the work on the mandible's teeth revealed no matches. The comparison didn't prove who it was, but it did prove who it wasn't.

The report went on to say the human bones recovered included two large fragments of the left humerus. There were also two different types of hair. One type presumed to be head hair; the other presumed to be facial hair. These hairs provided the clues that helped determine the race of the person.

Doctor Bass went on to describe the different formulas that helped him reach his conclusions. Miller was astonished at how Doctor

Bass was able to determine so much information from a few fragments of bone, the lower mandible, and a few hairs.

His report stated the person was over thirty years old, a white male, and had been dead between three months and a year, also that the body had never been buried. The time of death was the most difficult to determine. Bass said the fragments of the humerus exhibited a "greasy" look with bits of flesh still adhered to the bone. All the bones, as well as the shirt, exhibited a strong odor of decay.

Doctor Bass concluded his report by stating there is no evidence at this time as to the cause of death. He did, however, make an interesting observation about the remains of the shirt recovered. There appeared to be a horizontal slit in the cloth of the shirt above the hem line. There were other rips and tears in the shirt, but this particular rip ran perpendicular to the grain of the material.

Miller thought that even though Doctor Bass didn't come right out and say it, there was a strong suggestion this slit could have been caused by a knife.

Miller knew he probably had a homicide, but without an identification and a cause of death, he was at a standstill.

Back in Oak Ridge, Detective Landau knew who he was looking for, but was not sure why he was missing or where he was going to find him.

Months would pass before either of them knew there would be a discovery that would put both investigations on the same track.

Chapter 3

Horror in the Woods

Early one morning in the first week of
October, the phone rang on Landau's desk It was
Mrs. Keller saying that she and her husband were
coming to Oak Ridge. They wanted to pick up Jack's
things. They also wanted to meet Jack's friend
Brenda and get his mail.

Landau made telephone calls to Brenda Baker
and Danny Litton. They both would be available
when the Keller's would arrive in Oak Ridge.
Neither had any further information that would help
locate Jack.

Mr. and Mrs. Keller arrived as planned. They
registered at a local motel and drove to the police
station. Landau knew the task ahead of them was
going to be a difficult one. He wished he could give

them some hope, but it was as if Jack just vanished from the face of the earth. He feared the elderly couple would never learn what happened to their only child.

They drove over to the storage building at Elza Gate and paid the rent that was due. Inside they found Jack's drums, a few pieces of furniture, and some paint supplies.

From there they drove to the police impound lot and removed all of Jack's things from his car. Landau didn't know what to say to them, as he could see the pain and emotion on their faces. When they arrived at Danny Litton's house, they looked through the mail he had been holding. There was nothing of significance in the mail, with the exception of a letter from a girl in a juvenile detention facility in middle Tennessee. The letter generally indicated an affair between them. There was also a reference to another girl named Shirley in the letter.

The next day the Kellers met with Jack's friend Brenda. She was glad to meet them and sorry she couldn't shed any light on his disappearance. They left that afternoon, returning to Wisconsin without learning anything new.

Their hopes of locating Jack were growing dim and they were beginning to fear the worst.

When they returned home they received a call from one of Jack's friends in Milwaukee. Jim Taylor had known Jack since they were kids, playing stick ball in the streets of their neighborhood. Taylor wanted to know the name of the officer investigating Jack's disappearance in Tennessee. He did not tell them why he needed the information, saying only that he just wanted to talk to him.

Landau received the call in his office. Taylor explained, that he lived in Wisconsin and was a long-time friend of Jack Keller.

"I thought of something when I talked to Jack's mother after she got back from Tennessee, I thought I should pass on to you," he told Landau. "When I last saw Jack, back in June he told me about having an affair with two very young girls. I took it they were about fifteen or even younger. Anyway, Jack told me that he was thinking about moving back here because the family, or maybe just the father, I really don't remember exactly, of the girls threatened to kill him if he didn't stay away from them."

"Do you recall if Jack mentioned any names?" Louis asked.

"No. I don't. But I do know he was really worried about it. The way he talked, he gave me the impression that he felt these people really meant business. Anyway, I thought you should know about it."

"Well, I appreciate your calling, Mr. Taylor. If you think of anything else, please get in touch with me."

"I'll be sure to do that. I would like to ask you a question, detective. I don't know if you can answer it, but I'm sure you have a feeling about these things."

"What's that?"

"Do you think Jack is dead? I mean he always kept in touch with his parents and me. He's

37

never gone this long without calling. I'm really worried that maybe these mountain people, whoever they are, really did kill him."

"Well, I have no way of knowing at this point, but I'll tell you I'm also concerned that we haven't been able to locate him yet. I can assure you we're doing all we can to find him."

The Kellers spent the Thanksgiving and Christmas holidays at home without word from their only son. They made frequent calls to detective Landau. Not knowing what fate Jack might have met was taking a toll on the elderly couple. Regardless of where he was or what he was doing, Jack always called his parents on the holidays.

Although they never said anything to each other, the Kellers knew in their hearts that something terrible had happened to Jack. It had now been six months and all they had were their memories of his June visit.

The winters in East Tennessee were rarely severe. This winter was no exception. The nights were cold but the ground was snow covered for no more than a couple of days because of the warm-up during the day time hours. Each morning the winter sun's rays came streaming through the woods and cast a spell of magic through the air. In about an hour, the chill would disappear.

In the winter, the Reverend Luther Stern and his son James went into the woods in the bottom every Saturday morning to hunt rabbits. They both loved the solitude and peacefulness offered by their surroundings. After almost two years of hunting in the bottom, neither of them shot a rabbit, or anything else for that matter; even though the little creatures were running all over the place. For one thing they didn't want the blast from their shotguns to shatter the divine silence. They also both knew they didn't have it in their hearts to kill one of Gods lovely creatures. They received more satisfaction just watching them scamper around than killing them.

As Luther and his son wandered through the bottom along the creek, they became separated. Suddenly the silence was broken; not by a blast from one of their shotguns, but by a blood curdling scream from young James.

"DAD!" he screamed. Luther answered, but his voice was covered by the repeated screams of his son.

"DAD!" James yelled.

"DAD. COME HERE! HURRY!"

Luther could tell what direction the screams were coming from and started running towards his son, breaking branches like a bear charging through the woods with a pack of dogs hot on his trail. He spotted James on the creek bank and ran over to him. The look in the boys eyes was terrifying. He could not imagine what the boy could have seen in this tranquil setting that could have frightened him to the point of near hysteria.

The boy was panting heavily, and could hardly speak. He pointed in the direction behind them on the side of the ridge. "It's a...a...It's a."

"Over there," he pointed. "It's a skull!"

Luther looked at his son in disbelief as he

turned and scanned the hillside, but James insisted. "Come on, I'll show you."

James lead the way through the woods up the steep incline of the ridge. Suddenly stopping in his tracks, he pointed. "Right there it is. I told you. Right there it is!" he said excitedly. Luther examined the gruesome discovery, then told James to go call the law.

James hurried up the ridge and onto the roadway. There was no traffic in sight so he started running down the road to the nearest house for help. About a quarter of a mile south of where he came out of the woods was the home of Virgil and Martha Perkins.

He ran up onto the front porch and started pounding on the door.

Virgil Perkins was already up and outside, stacking some firewood around the back of the house. When he heard James yelling and pounding on the door, he came around front to see what all the commotion was about.

"What is it, son?" he said as he spotted James on the front porch. "What are you all fired up about, boy?"

"Virgil, you gotta call the law!"

About that time, Martha came to the door and they all went inside. "Now calm down, boy, and tell me again what's goin' on."

"Me and my dad was rabbit huntin' and found a person's skull. He sent me to get help. You gotta call the law, Virgil."

"Martha, call the law and get them down here

right away. I told you it would turn up sooner or later." Virgil was referring to the rest of the remains belonging to the jaw bone found in his yard months ago.

"Where's your dad now, son?"

"He's down by the creek. Just below the pull-off area."

Virgil left to take James back to the creek.

It seemed like just a few minutes and "the law" was crawling all over Frost Bottom. During the wait Luther carefully examined the site. He never touched the skull, but could see clearly there were, he was certain, two bullet holes in it. While he waited he also prayed. He prayed for the poor soul of the skull's owner. He prayed to God that the answers to the questions such as who was this person, and how did he end up this way, would come swiftly. He prayed that the burden of grief would not be to great upon this person's family and loved ones.

The first officer on the scene was Deputy Paul Wilder; the same officer who responded to the discovery of the jaw bone in Virgil Perkins' yard. Virgil recognized the deputy and walked over to him.

The entire area was sealed off by the officers. They knew at a glance the skull had two bullet holes in it. A good indication this was not a suicide was that one hole was in the back of the head.

Captain John Miller knew from the moment the jaw bone was discovered months earlier, there would be a homicide investigation launched. He remembered also Doctor Bass saying the body had never been buried.

41

When Miller arrived at the scene, he called for Detective Sergeant Danny Bonet to meet him there. Miller had become occupied with an unrelated investigation that was taking all of his time. He knew Danny would be quite capable of heading up this investigation. In fact, they talked in the past about how they would proceed in the event the remainder of the skeleton was found. The first order of business would be to contact Doctor Bass and get him and his team out to the scene.

Danny Bonet was a young, energetic cop. He had been working primarily on drug investigations, but was well schooled in other areas. Sheriff Collier liked Danny. He knew he was something of a maverick, but overlooked some of his tactics because he almost always got results that made the sheriff look good. That meant votes.

Danny Bonet was a blond haired, blue eyed, good looking country boy. He and his wife had been divorced for three years, about the same amount of time he had been with the sheriff's department. His thirteen year old son lived with him in a fairly new subdivision over-looking the Clinch River, just outside of Clinton. He was a no-nonsense cop. Many of the bad guys were fooled by his soft spoken manner until they tangled with him for the first time.

Bonet was a tough guy who feared nothing, and was not afraid to take chances. He was known to have a few beers now and then, but despised the use of drugs. He preached constantly to his son and his friends about the dangers of drugs.

If Danny had a fault it was that he sometimes

thought he had all the answers and didn't like to take advise from the other officers, not even the older guys.

Bonet could always be seen with his sidekick Bill Dalton. Dalton was not a sworn police officer or even a bonded deputy, but he worked very closely with Bonet setting up drug deals. He looked and played the part of a doper, and was actually the main reason for Danny's success. Dalton had an extensive police record himself, which no doubt would have been even more impressive if not for Bonet getting him out of jam after jam. Some of the other officers often wondered why Bonet relied so heavily on him, and even tried to pressure him to get rid of Dalton once and for all. Danny would just say Dalton was his good luck charm and continued to work him. Some of the other officers with years of experience working informants told Danny that some day the relationship he had with Dalton would come back to haunt him.

It was not a surprise to any of the officers that Dalton was with Bonet when he arrived at the scene on Frost Bottom Road. They weren't even surprised when they saw him helping with measurements and taking photographs of the crime scene.

As expected it didn't take long for the area to be swarming with curious citizens. Miller knew there was no way he was going to be able to keep this quiet. In fact he thought that now the proper use of the press might help them with the investigation.

Doctor Bass and his forensic team arrived in about an hour. The officers were impressed at the way they went about their work. Each one of them carried a roll of toilet paper. When they located a bone or bone fragment, they encircled it with the tissue. Photographs of their findings were taken before anything was moved. An overall view of the area showed how the bones were scattered over the side of the ridge for about a hundred yards.

The search was methodical. As a result, almost the entire skeleton was recovered. The bones discovered were in good shape. The skull was completely intact, except for the lower mandible being missing.

There wasn't much guess work required to form an opinion as to the cause of death. The skull contained two bullet holes that were clearly visible. One bullet entered the back of the head and exited through the left eye. The other bullet entered the right temple, and went completely through the head. Both bullets fracturing and fragmenting the bone as they exited.

During the search of the area, they located several large bones and some clothing articles, including an unusual belt at the base of a large pine tree.

"I'm quite sure the area under the pine tree is the point of origin," Bass told the officers. "We have checked closely and that's where we found the victim's hair. The hair is the first thing to fluff off during decomposition of a body," Bass explained. "We also found a pair of sun glasses next to the hair, and a pair of leather, flip flop type shoes. I think we should check this area closely for shell casings or bullets too."

They carefully cleared the area of leaves and brush, and within a few minutes found a brass shell casing and a lead bullet. After all the photographs were taken, they gathered all the evidence. Bonet and his sidekick Dalton took measurements and drew a detailed sketch of the crime scene, including the pull-off area along Frost Bottom Road. There was an old logging road about ten feet below the pull-off area. The terrain then dropped off sharply, leveling off just before it reached the creek. The largest amount of evidence was found about half way between the logging road and the creek. Doctor Bass said that was because the remains were scattered by animals.

Back at the roadway Captain Miller introduced Danny to Doctor Bass, and advised him Danny would be the lead investigator in the case.

"Well, guys what do you think?" Miller asked everybody that was standing around.

"I'll tell you one thing for sure," Bonet said. "This guy damn sure didn't shoot himself twice in the head."

"Yeah, and the poor bastard probably didn't even know it was coming. I'll bet the first one was in the back of the head." Dalton had to make his opinion known. Miller gave him a dirty look.

"Yeah, it's almost like execution style," Danny said to get Miller's attention off of Dalton.

"Well, I'm certain the area under the pine tree is where he was killed," Doctor Bass said. "And I'm sure the mandible we have belongs to him. I'll do some tests and further evaluation when I get these things back to the university."

"He must not be local, or we'd have a missing person report," Miller said.

"Yeah, that could make things a little harder. Hell, for all we know he could be from California," Bonet said.

"I think we should start with the newspapers and try to get something on him. Shit, you know there's that chance we'll never I D him," Miller said as he walked over to his car. "Roane County has one they found in a dumpster four years ago and still ain't got a clue as to who the hell she is."

When Bonet advised the dispatcher he was finished at the scene and returning to the station, she told him that Detective Landau from Oak Ridge wanted him to call him right away. Bonet stopped at a pay phone in River City and called the Oak Ridge Police Department.

"Hey Louis, this is Danny Bonet."

"I heard you guys found some bones down in Frost Bottom. Anything to it?" Louis asked.

"Yeah, we just finished up out there. Doctor Bass came out from U. T. He's got all the stuff with him. He's gonna try to help us identify him. Looks like he was shot in the head."

"Danny, can you come by the station before you head back to Clinton? I've got a feeling we just might be able to help each other on this one."

"Whatta ya mean, Louis?"

"Well, I've been working a missing person case since the fall. A guy who lived in Oak Ridge."

"No shit! How come he wasn't entered in the computer?"

"Well, the captain took the report, then asked me to look into it. I thought he entered him, and he thought I did. Turns out, nobody entered him," Louis said.

"Jesus Christ, Louis, we had this guy's jaw bone since sometime in August. Sure would have been nice if we knew about your guy."

"How come nobody knew about you finding the jaw bone?" Louis said in defense of their mistake.

"Well, all that don't matter now. What we need to do is work together and see if it's the same guy," Danny said. "I'll be there in about fifteen minutes, Louis."

When he got back in the car he told Dalton what Landau wanted. "Sounds like somebody screwed up to me." Dalton had to get his two cents in. Danny didn't respond.

When Bonet arrived in Oak Ridge, he went directly to the police department. He looked over Landau's report and was almost certain it was the same guy. When he saw the photograph sent by Keller's mother, he was positive.

"Jesus, Louis, he's wearing the same belt we found out in the woods. Look here. It's even got the double row of holes. I ain't never seen another one like it. Can I use the phone?"

Danny called the sheriff's office and spoke to Captain Miller. "Hey John, can I get a raise?"

"What?"

"Well, since I already found out who your skeleton friend is I figured I oughta get a raise," Danny said jokingly.

"What the Hell are you talking about, Danny?"

"Don't get pissed, but I'm at the Oak Ridge P. D. talking to Louis Landau. He's been working a missing person since the fall. I'm sure it's the same guy."

"You're sure?"

"Yeah, I'm looking at this guy's picture. He's even wearing the same belt as we found at the scene." Danny was getting excited.

"Jesus Christ! Why the Hell didn't we know anything about this missing person?" he snapped. "We are in the same Goddamn county you know."

"Take it easy John. I'll fill you in on that when I get back. The important thing now is I think we should be working with Oak Ridge on this. At least until we find out for sure what happened."

Since there was little doubt that the missing person and the Frost Bottom skeleton were one and the same, the two departments agreed to work in consort for a while. There were a lot of unanswered questions. The most important being how to make positive identification of the skeletal remains.

Bonet called Doctor Bass and filled him in on the latest developments. He suggested they contact Jack Keller's parents and try to find out who his dentist was. They still had the mandible with the six teeth in it, and that would be the quickest and easiest way to make positive identification.

Since Landau had contact with the Kellers he agreed to make the call. He wasn't too keen on the idea of having to explain to them that their son may be a pile of bones that were scattered all over the woods.

Chapter 4

Skeletons Can Talk

The most difficult task a police officer is called upon to do is notifying the next of kin concerning the death of a loved one. Although Louis had not confirmed the death of Jack Keller, having to call his parents and ask them for medical records so they could be compared to the skeletal remains was extremely hard for him.

Mrs. Keller was upset when she was talking to Landau, but she did remember that he had hurt his shoulder twice and went to the hospital in both Oak Ridge and Milwaukee.

When Louis hung up the phone, he looked across the desk at Bonet and said, "You know, I wonder if it would be easier on them if it does turn out to be their son. If it was then at least the anxiety would be over. You know what I mean?"

"Yeah, I guess it would be a bitch waitin' to see if your missing son turns out to be a skeleton that was found out in the woods," Danny said. "Jesus, I really feel sorry for those people."

"Anyway, we need to check with Oak Ridge Hospital. She told me Jack was there a while back because he hurt his shoulder. She's pretty sure they took some x-rays," Louis said.

Louis drove over to the hospital. Danny and his sidekick went back to the sheriff's office he wanted to get the paperwork ready to submit the shell casing and the bullet found at the scene to the lab.

Danny was at his desk when the telephone rang. It was Landau. "We just might be in luck, Danny. The hospital located the x-rays Keller had taken when he hurt his shoulder. I talked to a radiologist and he looked at them while I was there. He said there were no broken bones, but there was a shoulder separation. I hope Doctor Bass can tell something from it."

"Boy, that's great. I'll get a deputy to pick them up from you and take them over to him."

"Okay, I'll leave them with the dispatcher. I'm going over to where he lived and talk to some more of the tenants. Maybe I'll find someone else who knew him. I'm gonna go back to River City and talk to this guy named Litton too. He's a friend of Jack's who's been getting his mail. The last time I talked to him, I got a feeling there was something he wasn't telling me."

Danny went to report the latest developments to the sheriff. Vernon Collier, was in his late fifties. He had retired as a lieutenant from the Highway Patrol and ran for sheriff. Some people thought he was a good sheriff, while others didn't like the fact that shortly after he took office he hired his sister-in-law, his nephew, and his step-son. They were all qualified for their jobs, but that was taking nepotism a little too far.

Collier was a very distinguished looking man, not showing his signs of aging. He liked to dress well, and often wore neatly pressed blue jeans which gave him a younger appearance. When he wore a three piece suit, he really looked like the sheriff. He liked people and spent a lot of time with someone cornered in the courthouse hallway, telling them old highway patrol war stories or a dirty joke he heard at the sheriff's association meeting in Nashville.

Collier had been a police officer for many years, but now he was also a politician.

Bonet liked Sheriff Collier and found him easy to work for, although, he also wondered just how honest Collier really was. Danny was familiar with some of the sheriff's friends and felt strongly they were of questionable character. He had also seen the sheriff get angry before, and Miller already warned him he wasn't happy about working with the Oak Ridge Police Department on this case.

The Sheriff and the Oak Ridge Police Chief didn't get along. The chief thought he was a crooked sheriff and usually went out of his way to distance himself from him.

The sheriff's office was on the third floor of the courthouse. When Danny went up, the secretary and the records clerk, who occupied the outer office, were already gone for the day. Collier was sitting in his office and gestured for Danny to come in.

"What have we got out there in Frost Bottom, Danny?"

"About all we've got right now is a pile of bones. Doctor Bass and his people recovered almost the entire skeleton. He's taking it back to Knoxville to see what he can come up with. I've been to oak Ridge and Louis Landau is working on it with me."

"Yeah, I know. I still can't believe they had that missing person for months and didn't tell us a damn thing about it."

Danny answered quickly because he wasn't interested in listening to Collier get started on the Oak Ridge Police Chief. "We're pretty sure the bones are going to turn out to be a guy named Jack Keller who lived in Oak Ridge. We really don't know much more than that right now. Except it looks like he was shot twice in the head."

"Well, let's get him identified as soon as we can and get Oak Ridge out of this. We need to solve this one quickly. I don't want this guy's bones haunting me when the election rolls around. The press will kill me with it. You know what I mean, Danny? I've got to think about that shit you know."

"I think this is going to be a tough one." Bonet wanted the sheriff to know you just can't solve a murder quickly because an election was near. He knew this case had all the signs of being difficult to solve, and it was going to take some time.

"Get that useless son-of-a-bitch Dalton out on the streets in Oak Ridge and let him see what he can find out about it. Shit, he ought to fit right in with all those scum bags."

"Use anybody you need. Just get me some results as soon as you can. Shit, that guy lived in Oak Ridge. Why the Hell couldn't that damn skeleton have been found in Oak Ridge city limits so we wouldn't have to fuck with it?" Collier said. "After all the police chief doesn't have to run for his office."

"I'll do the best I can, sheriff." Danny couldn't wait to get out of his office.

"One more thing. Make sure you stay in the forefront. I don't want Oak Ridge getting any of the credit when it's solved." Collier had information that he was going to be opposed in the next election by an Oak Ridge police sergeant.

"What did the old man have to say?" Dalton asked when Danny got back to the office.

"You really don't want to know."

Danny was surprised by the sheriff's attitude. He didn't know the sheriff could be so callus. He was more concerned about the election than the poor guy who somehow got himself shot twice in the head.

55

Meanwhile, Louis Landau was talking to Danny Litton again. Since he first talked to Litton, Louis felt he wasn't being told everything Litton knew.

This time Louis made it clear Litton better not be holding out on him. When he informed him about the skeletal remains being found, Louis was surprised by Litton's reaction.

"JESUS CHRIST!" Litton said. "I knew this was going to happen. I just knew it."

"I think you better start from the beginning, Danny, and tell me what you left out."

"Oh man. Shot in the head. Jesus Christ! Okay...Okay..., I'm sorry I didn't tell you this before. But to tell you the truth, I thought Jack just left town for a while. I really wasn't sure he would be killed." Litton was walking in circles all around the room and sweat formed on his forehead.

"I think I should read you your rights before you say anything else, Danny."

"No, that won't be necessary. It's nothing like that. Shit, I didn't have anything to do with him getting killed. It's just that I didn't tell you before because I didn't want him to get in any trouble. And I really did think he just left town. I guess it don't matter now. See it's like this. Jack was quite a ladies man. The smoothest talking guy I ever met. He could talk any woman into his bed. Anyway, he started fooling around with these two real young girls. They were only about fourteen or fifteen or so. They got drunk a couple of times and he got them both in bed at the same time. I tried to tell him

56

they could get him for rape or something, but he wouldn't listen."

"Anyway, one day he came to me and told me the oldest girl was actually married to some hillbilly. Her husband came to Jack's house one night with some of his brothers and threatened to kill him if he didn't stay away from her. He said they had pipes and clubs and meant business. Jack was really scared. That's why I thought he left town for a while."

"How long ago was this, Danny?"

"It was back in the spring. May or June maybe. Those people really scared the shit out of him."

"Did Jack ever mention the names of these guys?"

"No. Not the guys, but I think one of the girls was named Shirley or something like that. I don't remember the name of the other one."

Landau remembered the letter that was in Jack's mail from the girl that was in the juvenile facility. She probably wouldn't be hard to find.

"Wait a minute. I just remembered. Jack was seeing this black girl too. I don't know what her name is, but Jack told me there was a guy who threatened him who was in the Klu Klux Klan. Jack said the guy didn't like him because he was Jewish too. If you can find out who the black girl is, she might be able to help. Man, I can't believe he got killed." His voice trailing off almost to a whisper as reality began to sink in.

It was getting late so Louis decided to call

Bonet and fill him in on what he learned from Danny Litton. They agreed to get an early start in the morning and try to locate the girl who wrote Jack from the juvenile facility.

They were both intrigued by the black girl and the threats from the guy in the Klan. It seemed like Jack developed quite a list of enemies.

Early the next morning Bonet received a call from Doctor Bass. Bass told him he attempted to make a positive identification from the Oak Ridge x-ray, but was unsuccessful because the left humerus had been destroyed by animals. He said the scapula outlines appeared similar, however, identifying morphological features were masked by other bones and tissue, because of the position of his shoulder when the x-ray was taken.

Bonet advised Doctor Bass that an x-ray that was taken in 1970 in Milwaukee was being sent directly to the university office. They both hoped that one would have what he needed to make the identification.

Bonet drove over to Oak Ridge and filled Landau in on what Doctor Bass said about the identification.

"Well, Louis, where do you think we should start?"

"I think we should locate this young girl Keller was seeing."

After a few phone calls he learned that Wanda Sue Morrison was now living back at home with her parents in River City. When they located the house, there was no need to introduce themselves. The law was no stranger to the Morrison clan. The only member of the family that had never been in trouble with the law was the mother.

Wanda Sue knew she was in no recent trouble with the law so she didn't mind talking with the two detectives. In fact she was curious as to why they wanted to talk to her.

"Wanda, I'm Detective Bonet with the Sheriff's Department and this is Detective Landau with the Oak Ridge Police Department. We're looking into the disappearance of a man named Jack Keller. We have reason to believe you know him."

Wanda was quite mature beyond her years. They had to be careful they didn't lose sight of the fact that they had to conduct this interview in a special manner. They realized talking to a fourteen year old female about the murder of a thirty-five year old man who was her lover, was going to have to be handled tactfully.

"Yes, I know Jack," Wanda said. "What do you mean he disappeared?"

"When was the last time you saw Jack?" Bonet asked.

"I guess it's been more than six months ago. I saw him in Oak Ridge just before I was sent off to Taft. I wrote him a letter while I was there, but he never wrote me back," she said. Her brow wrinkled because of the quizzical look on her face. "What's going on with Jack? Would you mind telling me what's going on?" She didn't like cops and was getting impatient with Bonet and Landau.

"Jack has not been seen since the early part of July. We haven't made a positive identification yet, but we're pretty sure that a skeleton that was found the other day was Jack Keller's. Now I want you to understand that we're here to ask the questions. The best thing you can do is cooperate and completely honest with us," Landau said in his official police tone of voice. He had a way of getting the attention of the person he was interviewing.

"Now, you said you knew him. Tell us about that," Landau said as he re-adjusted his tone.

"Well, I kinda like been to his house a few times. He was real good to me and my sister."

"Your sister knows Jack, too?"

"Yeah, Shirley was the one who brought me to his house."

"How old is Shirley?" Landau asked.

"She's a year older than me. She's fifteen, goin' on sixteen."

"How did you girls come to meet him?" Bonet asked.

"Well, about a year or so ago me and Shirley was in Oak Ridge just messin' around. Jack was painting a sign for some store. We started talking and then we went on about our business. The next day we saw him again and talked to him again. I didn't think no more about it 'til about a week or so later. Shirley told me she had been to his house. She started seeing him pretty regular. If you know what I mean."

"Shirley said Jack told her his dream would

be to have sex with both of us at the same time. We was there one day and was all drinking. Anyway, we all got pretty drunk and we both ended up in the bed with him."

The two detectives looked at each other. Neither said a word. They could not help but wonder what kind of family life this child experienced to have caused her to grow up so quickly. Then they figured they really didn't want to know the details.

"Okay, then how long did this type of relationship last with Jack?" Bonet asked.

"We just did that a couple of times. Until I started gettin' real nervous when Jack started taking pictures."

"Pictures. What kind of pictures Wanda?"

"He took pictures of us without any clothes on. Then he wanted to take pictures of each other having sex with him. That's when I decided not to go back anymore. Besides that's when our dad found out and he got real pissed. But Shirley kept seeing him. I think she was falling in love with him. She told me lots of times Jack treated her better than Eddie did."

"Who's Eddie?"

"Eddie Hooks. He's Shirley's old man,"

"Wait a minute," Bonet said. "Let's go back to something for a minute. You said your dad found out. Do you mean he found out you were having sex with this guy and he was taking pictures of you and your sister? Do you know if your dad ever reported this to the police?"

61

"Oh no, Daddy would never do that 'cause he hates cops and said he would take care of it himself."

"What did he mean by that?"

"Daddy said he would kill him if he found out it was really true. When he asked us about it we said it wasn't true, but he didn't believe us."

When Louis asked about where were Shirley and Eddie, Wanda replied, "Shirley's in Ohio somewhere and Eddie lives down on Spring Street in River City."

"Did Eddie ever found out about Shirley and Jack?"

"Jack told me that one night Eddie and his brothers, Jimmy and Darrell went to his apartment and beat the shit out of him. I'm sure he thought Eddie was serious 'cause Eddie told him he would if he didn't stay away from Shirley."

They asked Wanda to get in touch with Shirley and ask her to talk to them.

As they were leaving they asked Mr. Morrison to come outside with them. "I'd like to ask you a couple of questions, Mr. Morrison," Bonet said.

"Let me tell you something, Mr. Detective. I did go lookin' for him but I could never find him. As far as I'm concerned that son-of-a-bitch got what he deserved, and I'm glad he ain't around no more to do them things to my girls. But as far as me killing the bastard; no. That ain't my style, the way he was done."

"Tell me, sir, just what is your style?"

"I would have gone to his house or seen him on the street and blowed his brains out with my shotgun. I wouldn't have taken him into no woods."

"Why wouldn't you call the police and report it?" Landau asked.

"'Cause I don't trust the law, and anyway we just take care of our own business out here," Morrison said as he turned his back on the two detectives and walked back into the house.

Bonet and Landau looked at each other. "What do you think?" Landau asked.

"I think he's full of shit. I think he's the type that would take a man into the woods at gun point just so he could see him squirm."

"Maybe you're right. I guess we should just add him to the list," Landau said. "Hey, while we're down this way let's go talk to Litton again. I still think he's holding something back. Besides, I want you to meet this fruit anyway."

Louis wasn't sure Litton was telling all he knew. He was right. Further questioning of Litton shed more light on Jack's life style; particularly his sex life style. They learned he dated several women at the same time. He also had Litton photograph them making love to him. Litton also told them that Jack had sex with a married woman while her husband watched.

Later that day they located Brenda and re-interviewed her. They asked her some very personal questions about her relationship with Keller. She never would admit to any kinky stuff.

When they arrived at the station, there was a message from Doctor Bass. When they called him back he informed them he was able to make positive identification of the remains from the x-ray provided by the hospital in Milwaukee. He would have a complete written report in a couple of days. The next step was to call Mrs. Keller and give her the bad news.

"Hello Mrs. Keller. This is Danny Bonet with the sheriff's department in Tennessee. I've been working with Detective Landau on your son's case." Bonet cleared his throat. This was a difficult task.

"Mrs. Keller, I'm afraid I have some bad news about Jack's disappearance."

Bonet cleared his throat again before he could continue. "Doctor Bass from the university informed me a little while ago he has made a positive identification of the remains we found. He was able to use the x-ray sent to him from the hospital there in Milwaukee. I'm very sorry, Ma'am."

He hoped Mrs. Keller would say something because he could no longer speak. The lump in his throat was preventing the words from coming out.

"My husband and I have prepared ourselves for the worst, sir. I'll have to make some arrangements and notify the other family members. Mr. Bonet, can you give me any details? What happened to our son?" she said as she began to sob.

Bonet regained his composure and provided her with some of the information he had. She asked to be kept informed, and Bonet promised he would.

Suddenly, Mrs. Keller asked, "Can you advise me how I can go about claiming my son's body?"

The realization that her son's remains consisted of only his bones was difficult for her. There was no body. Bonet was not about to remind her of that now.

"Well, there will be some items that Doctor Bass will have to keep as evidence. I think maybe you should contact a funeral home there in Milwaukee and have them contact Doctor Bass at the University of Tennessee in Knoxville. I'm sure everything can be worked out, Ma'am." He had to think fast. He never considered these questions when he knew he would have to make this call.

"Man, that was tough," he said to Louis.

This was the first time he had ever had to notify someone about the murder of a loved one. It seemed even more difficult when he had to notify the victim's mother.

"You know, Louis, some day I'm going to call that lady back and tell her we got the son-of-a-bitch that killed her son."

"I know how you feel, Danny. I just hope she never finds out about all the aspects of his life style though. You know what I mean?"

"Yeah. He may not have been the greatest guy in the world, but Jesus, Louis, he didn't deserve to end up with two extra holes in his head and then be left to rot and have the animals scatter his bones all over the woods."

65

They both sat there in silence for a moment. Danny propped his feet up on the desk and ran his fingers through his hair, leaning his head back, looking at the ceiling.

"You know something, Louis?"

"What's that?"

"Just a short time ago all we had was a pile of bones. Then Doctor Bass got hold of it, and it seemed to tell him who he was and how he died. It really is something how Doctor Bass can get a skeleton to talk."

"Yeah. It's just too bad he can't get it to tell us who did it," Louis said.

Chapter 5

Suspects

Bonet and Landau both knew the key to unlocking this mystery was not going to found in the office on top of their desks. It was going to take leg work.

"Well, the hard part was talking to Mrs. Keller. Now what do ya say we go out and find the killer," Bonet said as he jumped to his feet. "Where should we go first, Louis?"

"I think we should go down to River City and see if we can find Eddie Hooks."

"You know that means we'll have to stop in and see Chief Larson."

"Yeah. But I guess you gotta do what you gotta do," Louis said as he rolled his eyes.

River City was one of the five incorporated cities in the county. Actually the city limits were shared by three different counties. This sometimes complicated things for law enforcement officers not familiar with the county lines. They knew what city they were in, but not what county.

The River City Police Department consisted of nine full time officers, several civilian dispatchers, and the chief, Charlie Larson.

"If anyone can tell us about the Hooks, I'm sure Larson can," Louis said. "I heard he runs moon shine,"

"Yeah, I've heard that too. But to tell you the truth Louis, I don't give a shit what he's into as long as he can tell us what we need to know." Danny's voice trailed off as he thought again of how Mrs. Keller took the news about her son. He was really determined to solve this case, no matter what he had to do.

Many of the people in the community jokingly referred to Chief Larson as Boss Hogg. He tried to come across as this hard working public servant, but behind his constant simile and sweet talking manner was a cunning, manipulating man who often misused his authority as a law enforcement officer to get whatever he wanted. No one can say for sure how he managed to survive attempts by newly elected council members to remove him from his appointed position time after time. Actually he wasted no time getting each new member in a compromising position. He was a master at it. If Boss Hogg was a real life character, he wouldn't even have been in the same league as Chief Larson.

"What brings the big city law all the way down here?" Larson said, as the two detectives walked into the police station.

"I'll tell you, Chief, we wanted you to show us just how things are done in your sin city." Louis had a great big grin on his face.

"You mean to tell me you guys ain't got nothin' better to do than to come down here and take lesson from me?" Before they could come back with another one liner, Larson said, I bet that's not why you're here at all. I bet you just might be working on the case where you all found them bones down in Frost Bottom."

"Chief, we need your help with something. I told Danny that you were the man to see if we needed to know something about some of your high class citizens," Louis said with a hint of sarcasm.

"Well, fill me in and I'll see what I can do for you." Larson lit one of his cigars and leaned back in his chair; propping his feet on his desk. He was all ears.

Louis smiled to himself as he thought how much Larson did remind him of Boss Hogg. He was sitting there with the buttons straining to pop off his coffee stained white shirt, because his huge belly was hanging over his belt, and his face holding a shit eatin' grin.

Larson was known for sticking his nose into everything that didn't concern him. Officers from other departments resented this and felt they couldn't trust him. Louis and Danny knew they had to tell him something, but had to be careful for fear Larson would want to become involved in their investigation.

"Chief, we're trying to locate a guy named Eddie Hooks. We need to know anything you can tell us about him and his brothers," Danny said.

"Now wait a minute, boys. You need to fill me in a little bit more." Larson put his feet back on the floor and sat straight up in his chair.

"Sure, Chief. We don't know a whole lot at this point ourselves. All we know is this guy Hooks may have been having problems with the victim. We heard him and some of his brothers may have beat him up a while back. We just thought it would be a good place to start," Louis said.

"Well, the Hooks live down on Spring Street going towards Frost Bottom. We've had trouble with that whole family for years. Each one is meaner than the other, but Eddie Hooks is by far the meanest of the bunch. About a year ago he got pissed off at one of his brothers, chased him up the road, and hit him in the forehead with an axe. Yeah, I'd say that probably would be a good place to start. And I'd say the ones that was probably with him when they beat this guy up was Jimmy and Darrell. They do whatever he tells them to because they're scared to death of him."

"Well, I'm not scared of him, and I think we should go down to the house and have a prayer meeting with him. Tell us where that son-of-a-bitch lives, Chief," Danny said.

70

"I'd go with you if I had the time," Larson said. "But I was just going to leave before you all came in. I've got something I need to take care of."

The two detectives glanced at each other. Both got the feeling Larson might be afraid to get involved with the case now. Larson gave them directions to the house and photographs of the three brothers from his files.

When Danny pulled into the driveway, he realized he had been to the house backing up the police department a long time ago. The house was a run down, single story, wood framed shack with tar paper patches on the siding and several broken windows. The front door was wide open and there were several filthy children playing in the front yard without any coats on.

Louis counted five junk cars in the yard and driveway, most of them missing body parts and wheels. Some of the cars didn't even have engines.

As they got out of the car, an older man with a sweating bottle of beer in his hand and a patch over one eye stood in the open doorway.

"What the Hell do you guys want?"

Bonet immediately recognized the man but knew him only as Eagle Eye. Eagle Eye Hooks lost his right eye years ago in a pool hall brawl when he was hit with a pool stick.

"How you doin' today, Mr. Hooks?" Bonet asked.

"I was doin' fine till you two pulled up."

"Well, I guess you already know who we are, so I'll get right to the point," Danny said. "We need to talk to Eddie, if he's home."

"He ain't home."

Just then a beat up old pickup truck wheeled into the driveway, behind the unmarked police car.

"You Eddie Hooks?" Bonet asked him before the old man had a chance to warn him.

"Yeah. What's going on?"

"Eddie, I'm Detective Bonet with the sheriff's department and this is Detective Landau from Oak Ridge. We'd like to talk to you for a minute."

"Hell, I ain't done nothin'. Whatta you want to talk to me about this time?"

"Get out of the truck, Eddie," Bonet said as he moved closer to the door. Hooks got out and slammed the door as hard as he could. "Man, I ain't done nothin'. Why are you guys always hassling me?"

Bonet knew right off he wasn't going to put up with Eddie's attitude for long, but he didn't want to piss him off more than he already was; at least not yet.

"Hey Eddie, cool down. You're not in any trouble. I just want to ask you if you know a guy named Jack Keller."

"Jack who?"

"Jack Keller. He's from Oak Ridge. Painted signs," Bonet said.

"I ain't never heard of no Jack Keller," Hooks said as he began to walk away.

Danny grabbed him by the arm. "Not so fast, Eddie. I just need to see your driver's license for my report." He had a feeling this guy hasn't had a valid driver's license in years.

Hooks pulled his arm away and thought about putting up a fight, but knew the two detectives would kick his ass and take him to jail anyway.

"I ain't going to lie to you, man. I ain't had no driver's license in I don't know how long. Look, man. Why you doin' this to me? I ain't never had no problem with you two guys."

"Well, you got one now. You're under arrest for driving without a license. I need you to turn around and put your hands on the truck, Eddie. You're going to Clinton. Maybe I can refresh your memory about Jack Keller."

"Go ahead and take me to jail. I don't give a shit. I've been down this road before. But I'm telling you, I don't know no guy named Jack."

Landau moved close and Bonet had Eddie in cuffs in just a second. Neither of them was in the mood for a foot race if Hooks broke and ran. As Bonet was loading him into the back seat, Hooks yelled to his dad, who was coming down off the front porch. "Just go back in the house and call my lawyer, old man. Tell her about this bunch of shit!"

When they looked, old Eagle Eye was stumbling back up the steps, careful not to spill any of his beer.

"Hey, Danny, drop me off at my office. While you're dealing with this guy at the jail, I want to follow up on something else. A while back Danny Litton told me about this black girl Jack was seeing. I also found out Jack had a run in with a

73

guy from Oak Ridge that was supposed to be some kind of a big wig with the Klan," Louis said after they slammed the back door on Hooks. "I've got one of my snitches trying to find out who he is and where I can find him."

"Sounds pretty interesting," Bonet said.

"Yeah, well there's some talk on the street that this guy killed Keller because he was seeing a black girl and that he was Jewish. May not be anything to it, but I thought it would be worth checking out. Besides, this asshole isn't going to admit to anything even if he agrees to talk."

Danny pulled into the bay at the rear of the courthouse and took his prisoner up the jail elevator to the booking area.

"Is that Eddie Hooks?" the jailer asked.

"Yeah, this is Mr. Hooks."

"I've got a message from your old man. He said to tell you the lawyer you wanted him to call told him she couldn't make it. She said you still owe her some money from the last time. She said you'll have to call someone else or apply for a public defender."

"Shit. Looks like I'm going to have to sit in jail on this bullshit charge."

"Tell you what, Eddie. After they get finished booking you in, we'll go down to my office and talk about a few things. Maybe I can help you with the bond. I might be able to talk the sheriff into letting you sign your own bond as long as you promise to show up in court."

Bonet was elated with the message from

Eddie's lawyer. He saw his opening and was going to take advantage of it; short of violating Eddie's civil rights, of course.

Meanwhile, Louis Landau was hitting all the low spots in Oak Ridge looking for one of his snitches. He found him at the car wash. He wasn't working there, just hanging out. The car wash didn't seem like a good place to gather. After all there was no food served there or vending machines. The only music was from the car radios of those hanging around. Unfortunately, they were not all on the same station. Louis knew however, the real attraction was the fact that you could buy any type drugs you wanted at the car wash.

Willie Maxwell had been giving Louis information for years. He was a middle aged black man who could always be found with a pretty young girl hanging on his arm. Even though he knew him for a long time, Louis never found out where Willie lived. He always just found him on the street. Actually Willie didn't have a home. He just shacked, changing his address every time he changed his woman. Louis knew Willie was just like any other informant. They only gave information when there was something in it for them. In this case Willie didn't have any use for this KKK guy and didn't mind passing along information to the police that might make the guy uncomfortable.

Louis spotted Willie in a group of young people and gestured for him to come over to the car.

"What's goin' on, Willie?"

"Same old shit, man."

"You got anything for me?"

"Yeah, man. I got something for you all right. The guy's name is Stinner. He's supposed to live over on the West side of town. You know, man, the side of town we ain't welcome in," Willie laughed. "I heard your dead guy did have a run in with him 'cause he was datin' a sister."

"You know her name?"

"Yeah, I know her name, but don't tell her I put you on to her man. Her name is Keeyana. Don't know her last name but she lives somewhere close to where Keller did. Anyway, my information is that Stinner went to talk to Keller about this black girl he was datin', and they ended up in an argument. I heard Stinner was goin' round askin' questions about him and found out he was Jewish too. Word was that was the last straw. I guess he had to show his Klan buddies that he was a bad ass. Anyway, that's about all I know right now, Louis."

"Keep your ear to the ground for me Willie. I really appreciate it. Don't get in trouble with all them women now," Louis said as he began to roll up his window and pull away.

"Hey, hold on man," Willie hollered. "One more thing, Louis. I just remembered. I heard Stinner always carries a pistol either in his car or on his self. I wouldn't want my main man goin' and gettin' his ass shot off. Never know, I might need a favor from him. Know what I mean?" Willie started laughing.

Louis drove back to the office and checked

76

the city directory for Stinner's name. He wrote down the address and was out the door again.

As he drove up in front of the house, he wondered if Stinner was really involved with the Klan. He lived in a nice neighborhood, and drove an expensive car. There were kid's toys scattered in the yard.

A neatly dressed, attractive woman in her late thirties answered the door. Louis identified himself and asked if Mr. Stinner was at home. Mrs. Stinner reluctantly let Louis in and called for her husband.

"Don, what is this all about?" she asked with a look of concern.

"I have no idea. What is it detective?"

"Is there some place we can talk for a minute Mr. Stinner?" Louis would leave it to Mr. Stinner to explain his visit to his wife.

"Let's step out on the porch, if you don't mind," Stinner said. "What's going on here?"

"Mr. Stinner, I'm investigating the disappearance of a man named Jack Keller, who was a sign painter and lived here in Oak Ridge. He came up missing back in the summer."

"What makes you think I can help you with that?"

"Sir, I'll come right to the point. I have information that you knew Keller and that you had some problems with him. In fact the information I have is that you didn't like him because he was Jewish and that he had been dating a black girl."

"That's ridiculous. Why would I care?"

"I also heard you had some connection with the Klan. Is that true?"

"We have a meeting every now and then, but it's not like people think."

"Well, wouldn't this guy Keller be a prime target for the Klan? I mean after all, he was Jewish and he was seeing a black girl. I would think it would be a feather in someone's cap to make an example of somebody like that."

"Wait a minute. I saw something on the news. You found this guy's bones in the woods somewhere. Didn't you?" Stinner said. "Well, I'm telling you right now, Mister, I don't know anything about this guy getting killed. Look, buddy, I've got a good job and a family, and I certainly am not going to screw it all up because of a jerk like Keller. No ...No. You need to be looking at somebody else for that. I don't have anything to say about that." Stinner was getting red in the face. Landau wasn't quite sure how to read him.

"So you did know him," Louis said.

"I only knew of him. We weren't drinking buddies or anything like that. To tell you the truth, I talked to him once. I found out he was a Jew and I didn't want anything to do with him."

"Do you have something against Jewish people Mr. Stinner?"

"I just don't have anything to do with them. That's all. Is there some law against that?"

"No, there's no law against that, sir. But there is a law against killing someone," Louis said as he looked Stinner right in the eye. "And it's my job to find out."

"I know it's your job, and I'm sorry I can't help you."

"You said you talked to him once. Can you tell me what that was about?"

"Well, I just kinda ran into him once. I really don't remember what all was said. I even knew the black girl he was seeing. But to tell you the truth, I didn't care about it. It wasn't my business."

"What was her name? Can you tell me that?"

"Yeah, her name is Wheeler. I think her first name is Kenya or something like that. She worked at one of the plants. I don't know if she still does."

"How do you know that, Mr. Stinner?"

"I don't know. Somebody mentioned it to me or something. I really don't remember. Look. If you're going to keep asking me questions about some guy who got killed, maybe I should talk to a lawyer. I mean, before I say anything else."

"Well, now that's up to you. But if you didn't have anything to do with Keller, why would you think you need a lawyer, Mr. Stinner?"

"I just know how you guys operate. You can trick someone into saying something they don't mean. That's all."

Stinner was worried about something and Louis sensed it. He had a feeling he would be back to talk to Stinner again.

"I know you're just doing your job, but I

really don't have anything else to say to you right now. I think you should leave."

"Okay, Mr. Stinner. If that's the way you want it. Thanks for talking to me."

"Oh, and if you have to talk to me again, please don't come to my house. I don't want to worry my wife with all this."

"Maybe you should call that lawyer," Louis said over his shoulder as he walked away. He didn't like Stinner and wanted to leave him with plenty to think about. He got into his car, leaving Stinner standing there on the porch.

Landau drove over to Holston Lane. He located a mailman who pointed out a duplex apartment where Keeyana Wheeler lived. It was unusual to find a black person living in this neighborhood, he thought to himself. When he knocked on the door, an extremely attractive black woman about thirty years old answered.

"Afternoon, Ma'am. I'm Detective Landau with the police department. Are you Keeyana Wheeler?"

"Yes I am. Is there something wrong?"

"May I come in? I need to ask you a few questions if you don't mind."

Landau stepped into the small but nicely decorated living room. His first impression was that this was a woman who worked hard for what she had, including the location of her apartment. He could tell she was comfortable here, even though it was not a black neighborhood.

"Miss Wheeler, I'm investigating the

disappearance and murder of a man named Jack Keller. I have information that you knew him. I'm only here to interview you as to what you can tell me about him. The more I know about him, the easier it might be to find out what happened to him."

"To tell you the truth I was going to call the police department after it was on the news. But I wasn't sure I needed to get involved. If you know what I mean."

"Yes, Ma'am. You mean about the race issue."

"Yeah. I just didn't know how involved it would get. It caused Jack some problems in the past, and I didn't want to bring all that up again."

Landau took out his note pad and wrote down her full name and date of birth. He would do a check on her when he got back to the station.

"I understand, but you need to be honest with me now and tell me what you know."

"Well, I did know Jack and felt bad when I heard about what happened to him, but I surely don't know anything about how it happened."

"I'm not suggesting that you do, Miss Wheeler. If you could just tell me how you knew him and anything you can remember about him, it would help."

"Well, I first met Jack about two years ago. He was playing in a band at this club I used to go to, and we started talking. In fact he took me home that night when I told him I lived on Holston Lane. He just lived up the street from here. We just became good friends."

Landau wanted to know what she meant by good friends.

"Did you actually date him?"

Keeyana figured Landau already knew the answer to that question and felt she better be totally honest with him. "Yeah, we dated for a while. I'd go to his apartment and he'd come to mine. You know."

"Did you know, or did Jack mention, any enemies he had?"

He was sure Jack talked to her about things that were going on in his life.

"Yeah. I told you the fact that Jack was seeing me caused him some problems. Well, I know about this guy he got into an argument with one time. He said the guy wanted him to join the KKK, but Jack said he wasn't interested. Anyway, the guy must have done some checking or heard Jack was dating a black girl. I guess the guy went off on him. If I remember right he said the guys name was Don. Yeah, I'm pretty sure it was Don."

"You said he went off on him. Did Jack give you any details of what took place?"

"Yeah, he told me it was late one night. He was leaving a club after playing in the band. He said he was getting into his car and this guy jumped him. The guy told him he knew he was seeing a black woman and that he was a Jew. He said the guy told him his friends didn't like that."

Landau was taking notes as fast as he could.

"When you say he jumped him, do you mean

Mountain Revenge

there was a fight?"

"No, but Jack said he thought the guy had a gun. He said he never did see one, but the guy kinda let on that he had one. Jack said the guy told him if he didn't stop seeing me something bad just might happen to him."

"Miss Wheeler, I don't want you to feel any of this is your fault. Jack was a grown man and made his own decisions. Besides, we don't know that this had anything to do with what happened to him. I'm working with a detective at the sheriff's department and he is following up on other leads right now."

"Yeah, I guess you're right," she said, half-heartedly.

"Did you and Jack stop seeing each other after that?"

"Not right after that. Something else happened that made me stop seeing him. I might just as well tell you about it. I don't want you to think I'm hiding anything from you," she said.

"That's right, Ma'am. This is a very serious matter and I don't want to come back here and confront you with something you withheld from me."

"Well, see, it's like this. Me and Jack was doin' fine. Then I found out he was seeing this real young girl. A while later, I found out he was seeing her sister too. I mean at the same time. Now that might have been okay with them, but not with this girl. Anyway, then it even got worse. Somebody, I don't recall who it was, told me that Jack was taking all these nasty pictures of these girls. One night I confronted him with it. He admitted the whole thing to me. He didn't even seem the least bit ashamed of it."

"Do you remember about when that was?" Landau asked.

"I guess it was about a month or so before he went back up north to see his parents."

"Did he ever mention the names of these girls?"

"No, he never did mention any names, but Hell, he showed me some of the pictures. Man, to tell you the truth I think he was sick. I really do. I think there was something wrong with him. I mean these girls were only kids." Her voice trailed off.

"Is there anything else you can think of that might help me? Any names of other friends or possible enemies?"

"Well, this might be something. One time when he showed me those pictures he told me that the girls' father, or maybe one of their brothers, I don't remember which, came to his house and got into a fight with him. I think he beat him up pretty bad. The only other thing is you might talk to his friend Danny. He lives down in River City."

"You've been very helpful, Keeyana. I'll leave you one of my cards. If you think of anything else, please call me."

"You know something?" she said as she walked him to the door. "Jack might have been a little strange, but nobody should have done him that way. He had some real good ways about him, too."

84

"Yeah, you're right. Well, thanks again and call me if you think of anything else."

When Landau got back to the office he called Danny at the sheriff's office, but he was still interviewing Eddie Hooks and would call him later. As Landau sat at his desk he had one of those gut feelings about Stinner. He wondered why Stinner lied to him about when he and Keller met. He wondered if Stinner or one of his Klan buddies knew more about Jack Keller.

He knew that Danny was really interested in Hooks, but he couldn't help thinking that Stinner was somehow involved with the Keller murder. Even though he and Danny joined forces, it seemed as though they were going in different directions.

He typed up his case file notes and called it a day. A long day.

Chapter 6

The Unreliable Informant

Danny Bonet had no idea how many times the telephone next to this bed rang before his fumbling brought the receiver to his ear. He was still half asleep, but only a few seconds passed before he knew the caller was Bill Dalton. He was really wired. Danny didn't know what he was on, but he was certain he was either very drunk or high on drugs; probably both.

"Danny, it's me, Dalton. Danny, I need your help, man. I'm in a world of shit."

"What's the problem this time, Bill?"

"Jesus man, you wouldn't believe what happened.   "I'm in the Knox County Jail. Oh man, what a mess." Dalton was almost hysterical.

Danny rubbed the sleep from his eyes and sat up on the edge of the bed. He was really annoyed with Dalton's rambling on, but not getting to the point.

"Slow down, Goddamnit! Tell me what's going on, Bill," Danny snapped.

"Well, I was at this gas station on the interstate. You know, the one at Raccoon Valley where the truck stop is. Anyway, this guy started running his mouth. Man, I really need your help this time, Danny."

"Were you driving?" Danny asked him impatiently. "Did they get you for D.U.I. again?"

"That's part of it. They got me charged with aggravated assault, drunk driving, driving on a revoked license, and a whole bunch of other shit."

"What do you mean aggravated assault?" He knew this was a felony and usually involved a weapon.

"Like I said. This guy was running his mouth saying I looked like a freak and a redneck doper. Anyway, one thing lead to another and I knocked him on his ass. Then he jumped in his car and took off up the interstate. So I got in mine and went after him. I guess somebody at the gas station got my tag number and called the law."

"I don't understand, Bill. That don't sound like aggravated assault to me."

"Well, that ain't all that happened. That's what I'm trying to tell you, man. They say I shot into the guy's car going up the interstate."

"What do you mean, they say you shot into his car? Jesus Christ, Bill, don't tell me you were stupid enough to shoot at this guy." Danny knew the answer to his question as soon as he asked it. He knew Dalton could be real mean and he lost any hint of good judgment when he got drunk.

"They got my gun and my car, Danny. I don't have no idea what the bond is. Man, you gotta come down here and get me out. You can tell them we got some big drug deals going down and you need me out," Dalton pleaded.

"No, what I need to do is take that gun and stick it up your ass and pull the trigger. It ain't even legal for you to carry a gun, Bill. I'm surprised they didn't charge you with attempted murder." The warnings some of the other officers gave him about Dalton flashed through his mind.

"You gotta get me out, Danny."

"You must be kidding. How the Hell do you think I'm going to do that, Bill?"

"I told you, man. Just tell them I'm working drugs for you."

"I can't do it any more, Bill. You've gone too far. I just can't help you on this one. You're gonna have to get out of this on your own."

"You mean to tell me you're going to let me sit here in all this shit without even trying to help me after all I've done for you?" Danny was taken by surprise and was getting pissed. He was aware now that he should have known this day would come.

"Bill, I'm in the middle of a murder case,

and the sheriff is really putting the heat on me to solve it. I don't have time for all the bullshit you keep getting yourself into. I just don't see any way I can do anything for you right now. If I did and the press ever got wind of it, they would kill the sheriff with it. Buddy, you're going to have to ride this one out without me. That's all I can tell you."

"I'll tell you what, you sorry son-of-a-bitch. Don't ever count on me for anything again. I can't believe you're doing me this way. I'll get out of this shit myself, and when I do I'll pay you back in spades. I don't need you. Just remember that. You were the one who needed me to make you look good on those drug cases."

"Bill, you don't understand."

Dalton cut him off. "Oh yeah, I understand all right. You used me and when I need a favor, it's sorry, Bill. Well, you understand this. Fuck you and your damn sheriff. I'll get you for this!" he said and slammed down the phone.

Danny felt bad, but he knew he made the right decision. All he had to do was stick by it. He never gave a thought to the threats Dalton made because he always ran off at the mouth when he was drunk.

He laid back on the bed with his eyes fixed on a spot on the ceiling thinking to himself that he should tell the sheriff about Dalton's arrest before he hears it from someone else. He jumped when the telephone rang again. He wasn't going to answer it because he was sure it was Dalton calling back. The ringing persisted.

"Yeah," he snapped as he grabbed the phone.

"Well, good morning to you too." He was relieved when he realized the voice on the other end was not Bill Dalton; it was Louis Landau.

"Sorry, Louis. My day has already gotten off to a bad start. I'll fill you in later."

"Sorry I didn't call you last night. I got in late and only had enough time to shower and change before we went to church. Anyway, how did things go with Hooks?"

"First thing was, his lawyer threw him to the wolves. She wouldn't come to the jail. He never paid her for the last time I guess. After he was booked, I took him to my office and had a prayer meeting with him. You won't believe this but he's agreed to take a polygraph test."

"Man, that must have been some prayer meeting. How'd you pull that off?"

"I just asked him and told him my theory on polygraphs."

"Oh yeah? What's your theory on polygraphs? I gotta hear this." Louis started laughing.

"I just told him if it were me, and I was guilty, I wouldn't take it. But if I was innocent, I'd want to have a chance to prove it and get the law off my back. So he said okay. He's not very bright, you know. Anyway, John Marcus with the T.B.I. is going to run him this morning."

"I hope it turns out the way you want it to," Louis said.

"How'd things go with you?" Danny asked.

"Pretty good, actually. I located and interviewed the guy in the Klan. His name is Stinner. First he told me he didn't know Keller. Then he told me he only talked to him once. The guy looks like a good suspect to me. There was just something about him. I don't know what it was, but I got a feeling."

"Yeah. I've got those feelings before, too."

"I also found the black girl Keller was seeing. She told me that Keller told her about him and Stinner getting into it. I think Stinner really hated him because of the black girl and because he was a Jew." Louis felt strongly that Stinner may be involved with Jack's disappearance. Especially now that Danny told him that Eddie Hooks has agreed to take a polygraph.

"I think he made some threats that he may have felt he had to follow through on or his Klan buddies wouldn't like him anymore. She told me about the two young girls, too. She knew about the pictures and some of their family members threatening him. I typed up my notes. I'll give you a copy."

"Okay. You want to meet me at the sheriff's office about eight? We can go over some questions for the polygraph test," Danny said.

"Sure. It's going to be interesting to see how he does. That is if he still agrees to take it after spending the night in that nasty jail cell."

"Shit, he'll be fine. I set him up with the best room in the house. Room service and everything. What could he have to complain about?" Danny said.

Talking and joking with Louis about the case made Danny forget about Dalton for a few minutes. While he showered, he started wondering what impact Dalton's arrest was going to have on the pending drug cases. The District Attorney had enough problems dealing with Dalton as a witness because of his criminal record. If he were convicted of anything else, his character and credibility would probably become an obstacle they would not be able to overcome. Dalton was really an unreliable informant, and Danny was glad he finally severed his relationship with him.

The Tennessee Bureau of Investigation had agents assigned to all of the counties in the state. Agent John Marcus was assigned to several East Tennessee counties. Marcus was not only a T.B.I. agent, he was also one of the few polygraph operators the bureau had to serve local agencies, as well as T.B.I.

Agent Marcus was an excellent investigator. His years of giving the polygraph test made him an expert with interviews and interrogations of suspects.

When Bonet arrived at the courthouse, Louis Landau was pulling into one of the parking spaces. They took the elevator at the rear of the building that went directly into the jail and sheriff's office. John Marcus was in the jail kitchen having a cup of coffee with the sheriff.

"John, it's good to see you again. I sure

hope you can get something out of this guy for us," Danny said.

"I'll do the best I can boys. What office can we use, Danny?" Marcus was anxious to get started. He didn't mind working with other agencies, but it did take him away from his own cases.

The detective's office was one of the smallest rooms in the entire courthouse. "This will be fine," Marcus said. "The only thing I ask is that when I'm giving the test, you guys wait out in the hall."

Bonet and Landau told Marcus all they knew about the case. Then Marcus took fifteen minutes to compose a list of questions Hooks would be asked. Danny called the jail and had one of the jailers bring Hooks to the small detective's office.

Eddie was all smiles when he came into the office. Partly because of the deal he made with Bonet, and partly because he knew the results of the polygraph could not be used against him if he were ever charged with the murder. The deal Bonet made with him was that after he took the test, he would let Hooks sign his own bond on the driver's license charge. Hooks agreed because he didn't want to spend a week in jail waiting to go to court.

"Eddie, I'm Agent Marcus with the T.B.I. Have you ever taken a polygraph test before?"

"Nope."

"Well, this is what will happen. First I'm going to advise you of your rights. Then we'll talk for a few minutes. I'll ask you some questions about your health and some questions about the investigation. The machine has a strap that will go around your chest, and there will be one around your arm. Kinda like when they take your blood pressure at the hospital. There will also be some wires on some of your fingertips. Don't let all this stuff scare you. I promise you it won't hurt. Do you have any questions?"

"Nope. But I'm telling you guys, you're wasting your time. I didn't have nothin' to do with that killin'." Eddie appeared calm, but there were small beads of sweat beginning to appear on his forehead.

"Okay, if you don't have any questions, we'll get started."

Bonet and Landau went into the hallway where they used the time to fill each other in on the events of the day before. Danny also told Louis about his phone call earlier from Dalton. He was interested in his opinion, and knew Louis would give him good advise.

"I'll tell you what I would have done Danny. I would have done exactly what you did. You needed to get rid of Dalton before he got you in a jam you couldn't get out of. I had an informant like him once. I got him out of a lot of tight places. But it seemed the more I did for him the more he tried to take advantage of me. I finally got fed up with him and told him to take a walk."

"Yeah, I know you're right, Louis. Maybe I should have listened to some of the other guys and got rid of him a long time ago. Now the drug cases

I got in court are going to be all screwed up. I'm sure the D.A. will have a shit fit too."

The conversation and a couple of trips to the jail kitchen for coffee made the time pass quickly. After about an hour, Marcus opened the door.

"Well, Eddie, I see you're still alive. It must not have been too bad," Louis said.

"When do I get out of here, Bonet? We had a deal," Hooks said.

"Just hold your water, Eddie. Let's see how you did first."

"How did it go, John?" Bonet was about to bust from the curiosity and anticipation of maybe getting something going on this case.

Danny asked the jailer to take Hooks out into the hall while they discussed the results.

"Let me tell you what I did here," Marcus said. "I ran him twice. I'll read you the relevant questions I asked him. Question number three was. Did you plan with anyone to kill Jack Keller? Number five was. Do you know who shot Jack Keller? Number seven. Did you shoot Jack Keller? Number ten. Were you present when Jack Keller's body was dumped near Frost Bottom Road? Number eleven. Did you have a .25 caliber pistol in your possession last June or July? Number thirteen. Did you ever threaten to kill Jack Keller? Number fourteen. Did you purchase a hand gun last winter? Number fifteen. Do you know if anyone in your family or the Morrison family was involved in the death of Jack Keller? Number seventeen. Do you know where the gun used to shoot Jack Keller is now. He answered no to all these relevant questions. The only one I feel he showed any sign of deception on was number five. That's the one that asked if he knew who shot Keller."

"That tells me he knows something about it." Danny was disappointed that he hadn't shown deception on more of the questions. "Don't you think so, John?"

"I think he's a pretty cool customer. I feel he knows all about it. Let's get him in here and squeeze him a little." Marcus was pretty sure Hooks wasn't going to admit to anything, but it was worth a try.

When Hooks was brought back into the room, they came at him from every direction. No good cop bad cop routine. They just bombarded him with questions, trying to shake him up a little. Marcus was right. He was a cool customer. He wouldn't admit to much. They did get him to admit that he knew Keller and went to his house one time with his brothers looking for his wife, Shirley.

Hooks denied ever beating Keller up, and held fast that he had nothing to do with the murder.

Danny told Eddie he could sign his own bond and get out of jail, keeping his word on the agreement. He did, however, tell the jailers to take a couple of hours with the paperwork. He had an idea and needed some time before Eddie got out and went home.

"Louis, let's go back to River City and see if we can find Eddie's brothers before he gets out. Maybe they'll come across with something we can go back to Eddie with later on."

"We'll probably get the same thing out of them as we got out of Eddie. Nothing. But it's worth a try."

During the drive to River City the two detectives' minds were full of thoughts about the case.

"You know if Eddie killed Keller, and he acted alone, we'll never be able to solve this case don't you?" Danny said sharing his thoughts out loud.

"Yeah, but let me run this by you. Marcus said the only question that Eddie showed deception on was the one about if he knew who shot Keller. Right?" Louis said.

"Yeah."

"I'm telling you I've really got this feeling about Stinner. What if Eddie had something to do or some connection with Stinner, and he knew he did it? Or maybe Eddie set him up for Stinner."

"I don't know, Louis. Wouldn't they be from two different worlds?"

"Maybe not. Sure Stinner lives in a fancy house and has a good job and a family and all that, but underneath all that he's just a scumbag. Just like Eddie."

"I don't know," Danny said. "I think the only chance we have with Eddie is if one or both of his brothers is involved and they come clean to save their own ass."

When they pulled into the driveway, they noticed two people working on one of the junk cars in the yard.

"Bet that's them," Louis said.

"I hope so. I really don't want to talk to old Eagle Eye again."

They walked up to the men and asked if they were Jimmy and Darrell. They said they were, but were not willing to talk to them about anything, especially the murder investigation.

Darrell, the taller one, walked up to Bonet and pointed with his grease covered finger to his head. "You see this, man?" He pointed to a nasty looking, jagged scar on the side of his forehead. "This is what you get when you talk to the law around here."

Bonet remembered what the chief told him about Eddie hitting one of his brothers in the head with an axe. No doubt this was him.

"So like we said, we ain't got nothin' to say. We don't have to talk to you less you got some kinda warrant. Eddie rules this place and he ain't here. So you better leave."

"Let's go, Danny. We're not going to get anywhere with these two," Louis said.

"Okay, boys, but we'll be back someday." Danny was pissed, but he knew Louis was right.

"Man, it's incredible how intimidated these guys are by Eddie," Danny said when they got back in the car.

"Wouldn't you be if he hit you in the head with an axe?"

"Yeah. I guess I would." They both started laughing.

While Louis headed back to Oak Ridge, Danny decided to go into the office and catch up on his case file notes too. He needed to report to the sheriff, but all he could tell him was that the case was at a dead end. Bonet was disappointed that the media coverage of the case didn't generate any new leads.

Danny was feeling a lot of pressure. Pressure not only about the case, but about the other cases he had pending. He thought again about Dalton, and knew his arrest was going to have a profound effect on the drug cases.

Chapter 7

Undercover

Time was passing quickly. Leads in the Keller murder case were few and far between. Bonet got nowhere with the Hooks brothers, and Louis had no luck trying to develop Stinner into the murdering KKK member he thought he was. Eventually they had to become involved in other cases. Danny wrapped up all the pending drug cases he had. Most of them were dismissed because of his informant's own problems with the law. He, like most officers, didn't like losing a case or having one dismissed, but he was relieved to have the cases closed.

His relationship with Dalton through the court cases was strained at best. Danny never asked him how his problems with the Knox County arrest were going, and Dalton never mentioned it. In fact Dalton only spoke to him when it was absolutely necessary. Danny was surprised that Dalton was still holding a grudge. At the same time he was relieved that he was finished with him.

The events of the past year were having a profound effect on Danny. A lack of concentration caused him to not follow through on many of his cases. He lost contact with Louis Landau and there hadn't been a new lead in the Keller case for a long time. He was losing interest in law enforcement and felt something was missing in his life. He didn't know what it was, but he did know he wasn't going to find it at the sheriff's department. He was frustrated by not being able to solve the big one: the Keller case. He felt the only way to get it out of his mind was to leave the sheriff's office.

He started talking about leaving and starting a painting business. Eventually he convinced himself that it was the right thing to do. Sheriff Collier was disappointed when Danny told him he was leaving, but he could see the energy and enthusiasm Danny once had about his job was gone.

"Danny, I want you to know that I've given this thing about your leaving a lot of thought. I think you really just need a break," Collier told him.

"I think you're right, Sheriff. I've already got a couple of pretty big paint jobs lined up, and I think the change will do me good."

"Yeah, but I want you to know something. It probably won't take you long to get burned out on this painting shit. If the Lord's willing to let me win the next election, you're welcome to come back here any time you're ready."

Danny felt the sheriff was really being sincere. He was pretty sure he would be re-elected. He was glad the sheriff would leave the door open for him.

By the time the election rolled around, there were four unsolved murders in the county. This didn't have much of a negative effect on the sheriff because the Keller case, by this time was pretty much forgotten. The other killings in the county were close enough to the election, that most people thought he needed more time to get them all wrapped up.

Collier was sharp enough to realize that if he was re-elected this time, four unsolved murders would certainly be an issue in his next campaign.

For now, he wasn't worried about it. His political maneuvering during the past four years was enough to get him his job back this time. He was unopposed in the primary and won the general election by a narrow margin. To Collier however, it was a great victory. He was already talking about holding the office until he, and he alone, decided not to run anymore.

The election was over, and in pretty short order, it was back to business as usual for the sheriff. Rumors that Collier was providing protection to several drug dealers were circulating throughout the county. The support he did have with the local citizens was fading fast. The local newspaper was actively engaged in trying to expose his illegal involvement with a local bail bonding company. This company was receiving about ninety percent of the bail bonds and the competition and many of the people wanted to know why.

The fact that the husband of the owner of the bonding company worked as a dispatcher at the sheriff's office was not a mere coincidence. He was in the position to know when someone arrested needed a bondsman. For a piece of the action Collier directed the jailers to notify this bonding company. In fact this dispatcher was known to actually make the deals himself while he was working.

Collier didn't seem concerned that the F.B.I. had recently been successful in other counties with investigations of other sheriffs involved with similar scams. Their supplemented salaries, through kickbacks and payoffs, landed several East Tennessee Sheriffs in a federal penitentiary. Collier was confident that his organization was tight-knit and secure from outside intervention.

Many of the citizens began to wonder why none of the murders could be solved. The trail on the Keller case had cooled with the passage of time, and there were not any new leads developing. The people and the local newspaper were becoming convinced that the same would hold true in the more recent murders. The sheriff's office was not making any progress on them either, and when asked about it, Collier just said he could not comment on it.

It was not usual to have so many killings in that county in such a relatively short period of time.

After the murder of Jack Keller in 1980, the body of a twenty-eight year old mother of two children was found decaying in the woods along the bank of the Clinch River. The body was so badly decomposed that after the autopsy, the cause of death was listed as undetermined. In 1982 an old timer in the mountains was found shot to death in the front yard of his country shack. He was shot in the back with the single bullet passing completely through his body. The bullet was found in the pocket of his bib overalls. This killing generated the most interest because the victim's brother reported that there was five hundred thousand dollars in cash stolen from the old shack during the murder. People were astonished to learn that the old man and his brother, who lived there with him, had that much money and lived in an old shack that didn't have running water and indoor plumbing.

Adding intrigue was the discovery of the body of a seventeen year old boy just a week after the old man was killed. The body was found along the roadway only a few miles from the old man's home. His head was crushed by a blunt object such as a baseball bat. Many wondered if the old man's and the young boy's killings were connected in some way to the Keller case. There were only a couple of miles between all three of the crime scenes.

The sheriff's department said the murders appeared to have nothing in common. However, not everyone felt that way. Many people were concerned that the three killings occurred in the least likely area of the county. Some referred to the area as the murder triangle. At least, the fourth murder was on the other end of the county and in a more populated area.

Speculation and rumors about the murders buzzed through the county like a chain saw. Law enforcement was at a loss for a motive. To the investigators the only case that appeared to have a defined motive was that of the old man, if there was a robbery at all. Some of the country folk just considered the killing just plain old meanness.

The citizens in this remote area have always felt slighted as far as services went. They felt it was because there weren't enough votes in the area to be able to put pressure on the politicians. They thought the sheriff should be giving the area more attention and be trying harder to solve the killings. Certain that the murders would have been solved if they had taken place in the cities, they wanted some answers from the sheriff, and were not going to be satisfied with his no comment attitude for long.

Sheriff Collier was paying attention. He was paying attention to the bad press that was mounting against him. He knew if he didn't turn things around, his chances of holding on to the office, and making money through his scams, schemes, and kickbacks would be lost.

Around the end of the year, Collier thought the answer to his problem arrived when he saw Danny Bonet walk into his outer office one gloomy day.

It was like a light bulb came on when he

thought that Danny could come back and work nothing but the murder cases. Even if he made little or no progress, there would be the appearance that he was concerned and doing something about the unsolved cases.

"Danny, I hope you've come here looking for a job," Collier said with a sly smile on his face.

"As a matter of fact, sheriff, that's exactly why I came to see you."

Danny was surprised at just how easy this was going to be. He thought he would have to do a sales job on Collier to accomplish the first step in the plan.

"I just thought I'd come in and test the water about me coming back," he said.

"I've got to tell you, I've come up with an idea for all these damn unsolved murder cases we've got. I was just sitting here thinking to myself who the Hell I could put in charge of getting something going on these cases. The press is killing me because we haven't been able to solve any of them. There are four now, you know."

"I've been keeping up with it in the papers. To tell you the truth, I've been wondering myself what you were going to do about it, Sheriff."

"Those Goddamn reporters don't understand that you just can't comment on an investigation. You know what I mean, Danny?" Collier was looking for Danny to agree with his excuse.

"Sure, Sheriff. It sure would be nice if you could make some progress on some of them though." Danny was laying it on a little now. "Tell me more about your idea. Sounds like you might have something there."

"You bet your ass I do. I've got to think about an elections you know. It's a ways off, but I know as it gets closer these unsolved murders are going to haunt me." Collier was thinking out loud and sounded desperate. The thought of not being elected for another term really worried him.

"Anyway, I thought I'd make a big deal with a press release and all that shit. In fact I think I'll put two detectives on it. Can you start right away Danny?"

"I sure can, sheriff. I really miss it, you know."

Collier wasn't even listening. The wheels were really turning now.

"I'll tell you what, Danny. I've got a guy named Callo working patrol right now. He's been with me a couple of months. He's pretty sharp. He's been buggin' the shit out of me to make him a detective, anyway. I think I'll put him in there with you. He can work on all the bullshit cases and help you with the murder cases when he has time. Yeah, I'll make a big deal out of this. I'll tell them I'm assigning two detectives to the cases." Collier was pleased with himself for coming up with an idea that would combat the bad press. "Hell, who knows, you might even get lucky and solve one or two of those damn cases."

"It's a great idea sheriff. I know Callo. I met him a while back. He was the chief out at the city of Norris. I didn't know he was working for you. I think he came down here from New York a few years ago."

"Yeah. He came in a while back and told me things were too quiet for him in Norris. Said he wanted more action. He told me he was willing to start as a patrol officer, so I put him on. Now this might just be the right time to make him a detective. I think the two of you will work well together."

"It really does sound like a good idea to me, sheriff. I'll get with payroll and get all that shit out of the way today, and I'll be in first thing in the morning."

Danny went back to the dispatch office to discover that Callo was scheduled to work the evening shift. When Callo came in, Danny wanted to be the first one to tell him about the sheriff's plan to make him a detective.

He heard a lot of good things about Callo and was looking forward to working with him. He also wanted to get a feeling about him. He knew Callo was an honest cop and thought that he might fit into the next step of the plan.

Danny finished all the paperwork concerning payroll and insurance and realized it was almost three o'clock shift change. He went out behind the courthouse to catch Callo on his way in.

Anthony Callo stood only five feet six inches tall. He was a little Italian guy who, even after three years below the Mason Dixon line, hadn't lost any of his New York accent. Sometimes the good ol' boys in Tennessee had a little trouble understanding him, and he found himself asking the good ol' boys to repeat what they said, too. He was learning though.

Callo was a smooth talker and in a short time he'd developed several good informants and snitches out in the county. He was nicknamed Jake when one of the other deputies saw him trying to round up some cattle that wandered onto the highway. The deputy jokingly said he reminded him of a movie when John Wayne played a character named Jake. Before too long everyone was calling him Jake. Some of the deputies jokingly called him Big Jake.

Callo, his wife, and two children moved to Tennessee in 1979. He left his position as a welfare fraud investigator in New York state after three severe winters in a row. The cold and snow was getting harder to take every year. His wife had family in Tennessee and urged him to sell their house and move south. It was a move he would never regret.

The small city of Norris had a position as Chief of Public Safety open and Callo applied and got the job. Norris was one of the five incorporated cities in the county. The city was a quiet residential community with very little crime. Three years as chief there served him well as far as getting to know his way around the justice system and politics in the county. He needed a challenge that offered more action. To get in the position where he could use his investigative abilities was his goal. The sheriff's department would give him that opportunity if he could find enough politics to get hired.

Callo was a dedicated, hard-working, police officer. Honesty gained him the respect of those he worked with as well as those he worked on. People knew he would be true to his word. He never made a promise he didn't intend to keep.

Danny saw Callo park behind the courthouse. "Hey, Jake. How the Hell are you?" Danny said as he reached out to shake his hand.

"Well, I'll be damned. I'm just fine, Danny. It's good to see you again. How you been getting along?"

"Oh, I've been doin' okay. Listen, I wanted to be the first to tell you what's going on, Jake," Danny said. "Collier gave me my old job back. I got tired of painting houses and wanted to get back into it."

"Man, that's great. What are you going to be doing?"

"He wants me to work on some of those old murder cases. I guess he's already getting worried about the next election. Anyway, he told me he was going to talk to you. He said he was going to make you a detective and let us work together on some things."

Callo's blast of envy quickly subsided when he realized that Danny said Collier was going to make him a detective also.

"No shit! Man, that's what I've been wanting to do. I'm going up and see him right now." Callo was really excited.

"Hey wait a minute, Jake. Don't tell him I said anything to you. Make like you don't know anything about it. I'm sure he wants to break the news to you himself."

"Yeah. Sure, Danny. I know what you mean."

Danny laughed and just waived. He had a good feeling about him.

Callo was excited, but wanted to hide it from Collier. He wanted to act surprised when the sheriff talked to him. He didn't want to seem too eager, or let him know he already knew about the transfer.

He went into the patrol office and pretended to check some paperwork, trying to make sure the sheriff noticed him. He had his back to the sheriff's office when he heard Collier, who was standing in his outer office say, "Hey Callo, come into my office when you get finished in there. I need to talk to you about something."

"Sure thing, sheriff. Be right there." Callo was about to bust. The thought of rushing home to tell his family raced through his mind.

"Am I in trouble again?" he said as he walked into the sheriff's office.

"No. Not this time," Collier laughed. "No, I've decided to give you a chance as a detective. I've been pretty impressed with all those burglaries you solved lately. And you didn't think I even noticed!"

"Thanks, sheriff. I really appreciate that."

"Anyway, do you remember Danny Bonet?"

"Yes, sir. I know Danny."

"He used to work for me about a year ago. Did a Hell of a job too. I've hired him back and he's going to be working on those damn murder cases. I want you to go into it and help him with the other cases, and maybe you can come up with some ideas on these cases too." Collier made sure he told him he wanted him working on the murder cases too because the press release was going to state he was assigning two detectives to the cases.

Callo was elated. "Sheriff, I'll do you a good job. I'm looking forward to working with Danny, too. When do you want me to start?"

"Check with the Chief Deputy. Let him find you an unmarked car and see about the schedule."

He spent the rest of the shift switching from his patrol car to an unmarked car. He also took a trip to the mall. He needed to pick out a couple of blazers and some new ties. Since he would not be wearing a uniform, he needed to supplement his wardrobe of civilian clothes.

He arrived at the sheriff's office at eight o'clock the next morning and joined Danny in the jail kitchen for coffee. He was eager to get started, but had to have that hot cup of coffee to get him going.

Callo had established some informants and people that owed him favors. This allowed him to get started quickly. He never worked with Danny before and was not familiar with his style. It didn't take him long to learn that Danny was a maverick. He seemed to like working by himself, and he didn't share much with the other officers.

As a matter of fact Callo often felt Danny had his own agenda. He tried to share information he picked up on the murder cases, but got the feeling Danny wasn't interested. As time went on, he noticed Danny was spending a lot of time with the sheriff. He was also becoming close to some of the sheriff's shady friends. Callo decided it was not his concern, although he couldn't help wondering about it.

Two months after they started working together, Callo was in the office late one night by himself when Danny came in. He was acting strange. He seemed to be hyped up about something.

"You alone, Jake?"

"Yeah. What's going on, Danny?"

Danny's eyes danced all around the office. He closed the door and locked it. Then he walked over to Callo's desk and pulled three wads of folded cash, each wrapped with a rubber band, from his pockets. He laid the money on the desk and Callo could see each wad had a small piece of white paper with a name written on it. Then he took a one hundred dollar bill from his shirt pocket that had been folded into a small square, and began to unfold it. Inside the bill was a small amount of white powder.

"What the Hell's going on here, Danny?" Callo was spellbound.

Still without saying a word, Danny unbuttoned his shirt to reveal two tiny microphones taped to his chest. The wires were running into his pants. He lifted up his pants leg and showed Callo a tape recorder in his boot.

"Jesus Christ, Danny. What the Hell are you doing with that shit?" Callo knew from his glance at the recording device that the only people who would use such a high dollar recorder were the F.B.I.

Danny put his index finger to his lips, silently telling Callo not to say anything for fear the room was bugged. Then he said. "Let's take a ride, Jake. I need to go check on something."

When they got outside, Danny said, "Let's take my car. I know it's safe. It's checked everyday for bugs."

"Checked by who?" Callo asked.

"The feds," Danny said with a smile.

"Man, you better start talking to me, Danny. What the Hell are you up to? You better start telling me what the fuck you're doing with that shit all over you." Callo was getting annoyed and the suspense was killing him.

"Just get in the car, Jake."

When he started the car, Danny started talking. "I've been working for the feds since I came back to the department,"

"Let me start from the beginning. I was going for a walk in my neighborhood one night when a car pulled up to me and stopped. It was Ed Fisher with the F.B.I. I've know him for quite a while. Anyway, we shot the shit for a while and he came up to the house for a cup of coffee. We started talking about the sheriff's office and of course about Collier. I told him how I thought Collier was a crook. I was really getting burned out

115

on painting and I told Fisher I'd go back to working at the sheriff's department if Collier wasn't so bad. That's when he asked me if I'd go back to work at the sheriff's office working undercover for the feds. He told me to try to get my job back by telling Collier I'd like to work on the unsolved murder cases. Anyway, Collier beat me to it. He saw me and got this brain storm about me coming back and making a big deal for the press about working on the murders.

"Fisher wanted me to try to get close to Collier and his buddies. Neither one of us had any idea it would be so easy, Jake."

Callo was speechless, but he did manage to ask Danny why he was telling him about his role.

"I need someone I could trust to help watch my back. I'm trusting you're the one, Jake," Danny said. "I talked to Fisher about you already and he feels comfortable with it. Anyway, you wouldn't believe the shit Collier's into. You know Greg Long and Billy Joe Moran, don't you?"

"Yeah."

"Well, those packs of money I showed you, I've got to deliver one to each one of them and one to Collier. It's their cut from the sale of coke and other drugs at Bubba's Bar down on Highway 61."

"And the hundred dollar bill with the coke in it?" Callo asked.

"That's my fee for being the bag man."

"Bubba Tillis in on it, too?" Callo asked.

"Yeah. That's where all the action is, Jake. Down at his place."

116

"That explains something," Callo said as he began thinking back on something.

"What's that?"

"A couple of days ago I went into the bar and talked to Bubba. I picked up some information that he knows about the old man getting killed down on Hoskins Hollow. I think he's dirty on it. But anyway, he wouldn't tell me shit. Not five minutes after I left the bar, Collier was calling me to come to his office. When I got there he told me in no uncertain terms not to talk to Bubba again without clearing it with him first," Callo said.

"Yeah. I heard about that, Jake."

"Now I ask you, what kinda shit is that? We're talking about a murder case here. You know, I knew he was a crook, but covering up for a murder is about as bad as it gets, Danny."

"Listen to this. Remember when we got those two suitcases full of Quaaludes, and the case was dismissed?"

"Yeah. They got a court order and destroyed them. Didn't they?"

"Like Hell they did. They got the court order all right and made a big deal with the press coverage when they destroyed them. That was all bullshit," Danny said.

"Collier got this big brain storm. The night before they were going to destroy the drugs, they went into the vault, got the suitcases, and took them to my house. They went out and bought boxes of Rolaids and made the switch in my basement. No shit, Jake. They destroyed the Rolaids and sold the damn drugs down at the bar."

"No shit?" Callo couldn't believe it.

"That's right, man. But the best part is that the feds set up in my basement and got the whole thing on tape." Danny was grinning from ear to ear.

"Man, that's good work, Danny. How long do you think it will take before they get busted?"

"It's gonna take some time. We've got a trip to Vegas set up with Collier and Tillis. The feds will have their rooms set up with video and tape recorders. You know as well as I do these federal investigations take forever. Just be patient and remember, Jake, you can't say a word to anyone."

Callo knew this was big time and any leaks would not only jeopardize a federal investigation, but could cost Danny his life.

"Don't worry about me, man. Just let me know what I can do," Callo said.

"I'd say Fisher will be in touch with you. I told him you could probably put him on to some things he'd be interested in. I'm sure he'd like to know about that thing with Bubba Tillis."

Callo now knew why it seemed that Danny Bonet had his own agenda. He did. He just hoped Danny had not bitten off more than he could chew. He was sure Bubba Tillis and his partner in crime, Greg Long, had something to do with that old man's murder. It hurt him to think Collier could be covering up a murder. He wondered, if there was really a half million dollars taken after the murder and how much blood money Collier received.

Chapter 8

The Sheriff Gets Busted

When Bonet dropped Callo off at his car, he was so wound up he couldn't go home. For two hours he drove around the county with the radio blasting country music that he wasn't hearing. His car was in drive but his mind was in overdrive. Going over the cast of characters in his head, he started with Bubba Tillis. Bubba was a redneck, a big redneck, weighing in at well over three hundred pounds. Tillis was known for breaking a few pool sticks over the backs of those patrons who couldn't get along at the bar. He had a reputation as a gambler. The back room of the bar was the nightly scene of high stakes card games, attracting gamblers from Knoxville and the surrounding counties; Bubba more often than not the winner.

Billy Joe Moran was another colorful character. The fruit stand he owned just a short distance from the bar provided some of the financing for the bar when it first opened. Sheriff Collier and Moran were long time friends from the old Highway Patrol days. Billy Joe was not bright but he had the right connections, and he knew how to make money with those connections. Moran sold fruit through the front door and did his dirty dealing through the back door. He was known for always having a large sum of money in one pocket and bragged about having Sheriff Collier in the other.

Greg Long was the third musketeer. He wasn't to sharp either. It was Long that Danny Bonet first conned into letting him into the inner circle of their crime and corruption ring. Long convinced the others that Bonet would be an asset and could be trusted. Long and Tillis grew up together, raising roosters for cock fights when they were just kids.

Callo could no longer keep his eyes open, and his car was almost out of gas, so he decided to go home and get some sleep. When he closed his eyes he kept thinking about the impact Collier's arrest would have on the sheriff's office and the entire community. As he fell asleep he tried to imagine how the whole thing would play.

Working daily with Danny Bonet Callo learned the true extent of the corruption. The depth of the bonding company scam and how money filtered down to some of the jailers, shocked him.

He was amazed that Collier would let so many people know about the scam without fear of being exposed. Then he realized that greed often times overpowers good judgment.

Callo talked with the F.B.I. in depth toward the end of the investigation and testified before the federal grand jury in Knoxville. At times he felt the investigation was moving too slowly. However, when he was made fully aware of the entire scope of the investigation, how much time was involved in planning their moves, and in transcribing the hours of undercover tapes, he became more patient. There couldn't be any mistakes at this point. Everything had to be done right because of the danger to Danny.

One night Danny came into the office and Callo thought he looked pretty bad.

"Man, you look like shit. Are you Okay?" Callo asked.

"Yeah, I guess when you consider that I'm still living and breathing after what just happened, I guess you could say I'm okay."

"You mean with your case?"

"You know Condy Dixon, don't you, Jake?"

"Yeah. I know him well. He's with ABC."

"We thought it would be good to get somebody else in with me. You know the feds. They want insurance. Anyway, me and Condy have been friends for years, and I know he's honest. So I thought what better person to try to get in than an Alcohol Beverage Commission investigator. I figured they would jump at the chance to have him bought because of the bar."

"I would think they would, too," Callo said.

"Anyway, I brought him in down at Billy Joe's. Bubba and Long were there to check him out. We were in the back room just bullshittin' when Long says to Condy, 'You ain't wearing a wire are you Condy?' He says, 'Hell no. What are you talking about?'

"Bubba says. 'Well, lets just make sure.' and makes him take all of his clothes off."

"Holly shit. Was he wired?"

"No. We knew better than that. But then Bubba says, that they ought to check me too. Just for the Hell of it. I almost had a fucking heart attack. Shit, I'm standing there wired in stereo. Lucky thing Greg Long jumps in and tells Bubba not to be an idiot. Bubba says he was just kiddin." I looked over at Condy and he was white as a sheet. Anyway, we got the Hell out of there as fast as we could."

"Jesus Christ. I see why you don't look so good. You better go get a drink," Callo said.

During the federal investigation, Bonet and Callo made it appear to Collier that they were working on the murder cases, but weren't having much success. In reality, Danny was completely consumed by his undercover role. Callo was busy working on recently committed crimes and didn't have time to concentrate on any of the old murder cases.

Toward the end of the undercover investigation, Danny came to Callo with an idea.

"Hey Jake, I was thinking about having a party. Your wife has a restaurant in Norris. That would be a great place to have it."

"What kind of party?"

"A going away party," he said and started laughing. "The indictments are all done, and in a couple of days the feds are going to be rounding all these guys up. Wouldn't it be nice if you threw a party?"

"You know, that's a great idea. I'll invite Collier and all his buddies."

There was just enough time to get all the unsuspecting crooks together for what would be their farewell party.

Everyone on the invited guest list showed up, the party was going strong. Collier was getting drunk. He kept himself entertained by pinching the women on the ass as they passed his table and was telling anyone who would listen old highway patrol war stories. Meanwhile, another group was in the kitchen with Bonet and Callo.

"Yes sir, right here's my sheriff's department," Billy Joe Moran boasted as he patted the wad of money in his pocket.

Danny never quit. He was in the corner of the kitchen talking Greg Long into letting Callo into their group. He told him Callo had some money he wanted to invest with them and assured Long that Callo could be trusted. Long had a few drinks and wanted to show Callo how important he was.

"Hey, Jake. Let's you, me, and Danny go outside for a minute. I got something I want to talk to you about. I think you'll like it." Long said.

When they got outside, Long said, "Danny tells me you might have some money you want to invest somewhere."

Callo was taken by surprise. He got a wink when he glanced over at Danny. He knew to play along. Callo could tell by the look on Danny's face he was having fun now.

"Yeah, my wife and I got about twenty-five thousand saved. But I've got to make sure of two things. One is that it's safe, and the other is that I'll make some real money," Callo said.

"I can tell you this. With guys like you and Danny in, it'll surely be safe. And the more you can do for us, the more money you can make," Long said.

Callo and Danny were about to bust. They knew that at about nine o'clock in the morning, Long would no doubt be aware that his world was going to change.

"You like gold, Jake?" Long asked.

"Sure I like gold. Why?"

"Here's a little something from me to you," Long said as he took one of several gold chains from around his neck and handed it to Callo. "I'll tell you what. You stop by the bar about seven tomorrow night and talk to me and Bubba. We'll see what we can come up with."

Callo was amazed how easy it was to get Long to commit himself, although he figured the twenty-five grand he mentioned was some pretty good bait.

The next morning a score of F.B.I. agents swarmed the county. Within a few hours Tillis, Long, Moran, and the owners of the bonding company were all in custody. Agent Fisher led Sheriff Collier in handcuffs from the sheriff's office. Collier's head hung low as a reporter from the local newspaper snapped a photo of them. Many of his deputies looked on in shock. The county was buzzing within an hour of Collier's arrest.

The feds not only had arrest warrants, but had secured search warrants for their homes and safe deposit boxes. Callo was asked to assist with the search of Long's mobile home. In addition to drugs and cash, a large amount of stolen property had also been recovered. Callo couldn't help feeling sorry for Long's wife as she sat there watching the officers take her house apart.

In the weeks to come the defendants and their attorneys would learn the extent of the indisputable evidence compiled through the heroic efforts of one man, Danny Bonet. As a result, the defendants were almost immediately looking to play let's make a deal, but the federal prosecutors were playing hardball.

Callo experienced a sick feeling in the pit of his stomach when he sat in the federal courtroom and heard Collier enter his guilty plea and read a prepared statement about how sorry he was. Callo thought he was sorry, all right. Sorry he got caught. The others arrested were sorry too. They were sorry they couldn't squirm out of pleading guilty and getting long prison terms.

Callo had strong feelings about the integrity of police officers. Collier was the top dog, and Callo was afraid these events would cast a dark shadow on all the honest officers too. It would take a special effort on the part of the honest cops to restore the trust of the citizens.

Tennessee state law required the county commission to appoint someone to fill the unexpired term of an elected official until the next election.

One of the applicants wanting to fill the sheriff's vacancy was a retired F.B.I. agent named Ted Branson, who lived in Oak Ridge. Branson was unquestionably the most qualified candidate, and made a good impression during the interview process. He reported not only his law enforcement experience, but also outlined a plan he would implement to restore confidence in the sheriff's office. He also placed emphasis on the unsolved murder cases. His plan to start neighborhood watch and drug education programs played well with the commissioners and the citizens.

Selected as the new sheriff, Branson had his work cut out for him and knew the importance of keeping his word to the people concerning his proposed programs and the reactivation of the murder investigations. It would take a long time to re-establish the department's credibility and the people's trust. Knowing the press would be an important asset, Branson quickly developed a good relationship with them. He also knew solving one of those murders would help him tremendously.

During a personnel meeting, he announced his choices of supervisors for the different departments within the sheriff's office. He let them know what was going to be expected of each and every employee. After the meeting he asked Callo to see him in his office. Branson was aware of Callo's reputation for dedication and hard work, and wanted someone with his integrity in the forefront of his administration.

"You wanted to see me, Sheriff?" Callo asked as he knocked on the open door of his office.

"Yes. Come on in and close the door, Jake. I wanted to talk to you about these unsolved murder cases. I've heard that you've done some work on them."

"Yes, sir. I've been trying to follow up on some leads I picked up here and there, but it's been kinda hectic around here for a while."

"Things are going to be a lot different now. What I've got in mind is to let you work on nothing but these cases. I think we should take the oldest one first and not leave it until it's solved, or clear that it can't be. Then I think we should go on to the next oldest one and do the same thing. What do you think?"

Callo was surprised and flattered that the new sheriff would ask him for his input. "Well, Sheriff. I've gotta say I agree with you a hundred percent. I think the only way we can make any progress is to work them one at a time and without interruption."

"Good. I'm glad you agree. Now here's

127

what I want you to do. Starting first thing in the morning, gather whatever case file exists on the oldest case. I think that's the one with those bones down in Frost Bottom."

"Yes sir. It is."

"Okay, get that one together and get started on it. If you need one of the other detectives from time to time, just let me know and I'll arrange it."

"I think Danny Bonet has the Keller file, Sheriff. Is he going to be working on any of these cases, too?"

"No. Just get the file from him. I'm really not sure what I'm going to do with him yet," Branson said.

Callo wasn't sure what the sheriff meant by that statement. He heard that Branson didn't like Danny and was going to get rid of him. Rumor was Branson told someone he was sure Danny was using cocaine and was going to ask him to take a drug test. Callo knew for sure he wasn't getting involved in that mess. Excitement was mounting about the challenge he faced and he was determined to make something happen on the murder cases.

"Sheriff, I know that Louis Landau with Oak Ridge did a lot of work on this case when it first happened. If it's okay with you, I'd like to talk to him about it and maybe get him to help if he can." Callo was thinking fast. He knew if Danny and the sheriff were going to be at odds, he probably wouldn't get much cooperation from him. He thought that Louis Landau would be his best source of information now.

"That's fine with me. I've known Louis for a long time. He's a good officer and I'm sure he'd be glad to help you as much as he can," Branson said. "I just don't want Danny involved with your work. Is that clear?"

"Yes sir."

"Just keep me informed and let me know how you're making out."

"I sure will, Sheriff. Thanks for having enough confidence in me to give me this assignment."

"I've heard a lot about you, and I think if anyone can get results, you can. Good luck," Branson said sincerely. "Oh, one more thing, Jake."

"What's that, Sheriff?"

"Stop by and see my administrative assistant. He's got a new badge for you."

"A new badge?" Callo was puzzled.

"Yeah, your lieutenant's badge."

"I sure will. Thanks again, Sheriff." Callo was in shock. He never expected this opportunity, and least of all he never expected a promotion.

That night he called Danny Bonet from home.

"Hey, Danny. What's going on?"

"Oh, nothing. I heard things are working out pretty good for you though," Danny said.

"Boy, news travels fast. Don't it?"

"It must not travel that fast if you haven't heard what Branson did to me."

Callo noticed that Danny sounded depressed.

"Whatta you talking about?" Callo asked

fearing he already knew the answer.

"The son-of-a-bitch fired me."

"He fired you!" Callo said in disbelief. "What do you mean he fired you?"

"He called me in this afternoon and told me he thought I was hooked on coke. He said if I didn't agree to take a piss test, I'd have to leave the department."

"No shit!" Callo didn't know what else to say.

"Anyway, I went back to his office a little while later with my lawyer. We couldn't work thing out so I left."

"You think it's because you tried to be appointed sheriff after Collier was gone?"

"That's probably part of it. But I also think Branson didn't like it because I worked for the feds. I think he feels I'm a threat to him."

"So what are you going to do now?"

"Oh, I'll find something to stay out of trouble. Maybe I'll do some paint jobs or work undercover somewhere. Maybe I'll just start getting ready to run when the next election gets here."

"I think the whole thing stinks, Danny. I sure wish you luck, man."

"By the way, I left the Keller file with Branson's secretary. He told me you would be needing it. I had it in my car so I brought it up and left it with her."

Callo had almost forgotten that's why he was calling Danny. "Thanks. That's why I called. I really didn't know what happened between you and

Branson. I sure didn't know you got fired"

"It's got all of Landau's notes in it and it's got some pictures I took out of the scene when they found the skeleton. I always suspected a guy named Eddie Hooks from down in River City, but never could get enough on him. You might talk to Louis, too. He's got a gut feeling about some guy in the Klan. I forgot his name right now, but Louis felt pretty strongly that he is somehow connected to the murder."

"Yeah, I'm going to talk to Louis as soon as I get a chance."

"There's, no need in me telling you how to do it. I'm sure you'll do a good job, Jake. I really wish you luck."

"Thanks. I'm sure I'll need all the luck I can get on this one. The trail's pretty cold."

"Jake, take care of yourself. Guess I'll see you around." Danny really sounded down.

Callo felt almost as depressed as Danny now. After he hung up he thought back to the days immediately following the arrests and how much chaos there was within the department. The former sheriff's top people had been talking to the politicians hoping to have a shot at being appointed the interim sheriff. However, the people wanted to clean house and weren't going to stand for anyone connected to Collier being appointed.

Callo had been amused as he watched the power struggle continue before Branson was selected. Danny Bonet tried his best to be appointed at the time too. As far as Callo had been concerned,

Danny was nothing less than a hero. He compared him to the walking tall sheriff from West Tennessee, Buford Pusser, and the New York detective, Frank Serpico. He felt strongly Danny had at least deserved serious consideration for his efforts in putting Collier out of office. He didn't think there would be a book or maybe a movie deal like Pusser and Serpico, but at least a chance to take the place of the crooked sheriff he brought down.

As he sat there, he remembered joining Danny for dinner at a Knoxville restaurant shortly after the arrests. They had talked about the possibility of Danny being appointed sheriff. The mood started out upbeat, but soon they realized that the politicians were more ruthless and cut throat than the bad guys he brought down.

Danny talked about the rumors that were circulating about him using cocaine when he was in his undercover role. He told Callo he tried desperately to dispel them, but couldn't. Callo was at a loss to figure out why, after all he had done, he was being pushed aside. People just wanted him to disappear. Was it the fact that he was considered a rat, and could never be trusted? Or was it even a bigger problem that Danny had?

There were times that Callo suspected Danny was using drugs during his undercover role. He probably had to so he could enhance his credibility. He recalled that many times when he spoke to him, Danny just didn't act like the Danny he knew. Callo just considered it was the stress of the operation. He hoped and prayed that Danny haden't gotten pulled in by the very thing he was trying to combat. He wondered when he would see him again.

As Callo's thoughts drifted to the present, he considered the Keller case. He couldn't wait to get his hands on the case file and talk to Louis Landau. He knew this was going to be his big chance. He thought it was a shame that Danny would no longer have anything to do with the Keller investigation. After putting in all the time and effort, solving the Keller case was no longer an option for Danny Bonet.

Chapter 9

A New Beginning

The selection of Ted Branson as the new sheriff had a significant influence on all the employees at the sheriff's office. The new administration seemed to motivate everyone. Branson felt in order to recapture the confidence of the citizens, he first had to gain the support and trust of the officers and civilians who worked at the sheriff's office.

One of the first orders of business was to completely change the officers uniforms. He felt it was imperative to rid the department of any sign of the old sheriff's department. The idea also served to boost morale. He felt strongly that if the employees' attitudes were positive, their contact with the public would be positive.

Just as the entire department was starting over, so was Callo on the Keller murder case. He referred to the re-activation of the old murder cases as a new beginning.

The sheriff issued a press release concerning the unsolved murders. He wanted everyone to know he was determined to resolve these cases and see that justice was served. His outward optimism was putting a lot of pressure on Anthony Callo.

His complete review of the case file gave him a better understanding of the facts. He knew now just how difficult the case was going to be. The fact that months passed before the remains were even found made it much harder to develop suspects and locate evidence. He could also clearly understand why Danny and Louis were each looking at different suspects in the case. However, he felt that the passage of so much time might now work to his advantage. He was convinced that the colder a case got, the chances increased of someone who was involved talking about it. Often they feel more secure with the passage of time, and bragging after they had a few drinks is not uncommon. In some cases a person who committed a serious crime such as a murder must tell someone just to relieve their guilt. Callo laughed to himself when he thought that all he had to hope was that the guy he was looking for in the Keller murder was either a loud mouth drunk or a killer with a conscience.

When he snapped back to reality he began making some phone calls. The first call that had to be made was to Mr. and Mrs. Keller.

"Hello, Mrs. Keller. My name is Anthony Callo. I'm a detective with the sheriff's department here in Tennessee. I'm calling to let you know the status of the investigation into the death of your son Jack."

When Callo hung up the phone he could almost feel her pain. He wanted very much to be able to call her back some day and tell her he solved the case and an arrest had been made. If anything keeps him on track, he knew the tone in her voice during the conversation would. He was even more determined now.

The next call he made was to Louis Landau and made arrangements to review the case with him the next morning.

Since the press release appeared in the newspaper, Callo began receiving calls from people who thought they knew who might be involved in the murder. He also put the word out on the street to his snitches that he needed information.

The call that got the ball rolling came when Callo was working late that evening in the office. He was making up some notes on questions to ask Louis when he meets him in the morning.

"Lieutenant, this is dispatch. I've got a guy on the line who says it's real important that he talk to you. He says nobody else can help him, and he won't give me his name."

"This is Callo. Who's this?"

"Hey Callo. This is Arlie. Arlie Justice. Remember me?" the caller said.

"Haven't seen you in a while. Where have you been?"

"I've been hiding out, man. I'm sure you know the law's looking for me. You know, on a warrant for that vehicular homicide."

"To tell you the truth, Arlie, I didn't know that. I've been too busy lately to keep up with all that stuff," Callo said honestly.

"Yeah, I've been readin' about that in the paper. Anyway, that's why I'm calling. Since you're working on that murder down in the bottom, I thought I'd pass along some information I came across."

"Whatta ya got for me, Arlie?"

"Not so fast. I'll tell you what I got, and it's real good, man, if you can do something for me."

Callo wasn't surprised. He knew that's usually how it worked. He knew that Arlie wasn't a real bad guy. He's just a drunk. He remembered now that he was charged with drunk driving after an accident that killed a woman down in River City. The D.A. brought the case to the grand jury and he was indicted for vehicular homicide.

"What do you need from me, Arlie?"

"Well, I always heard you like to wheel and deal, Callo. I also heard you're a man of your word."

"I try my best to treat people right."

"Well, I know the law is watching my house. I think they're following my wife too. Anyway, I decided I can't keep going like I am. I want to turn myself in. But, I want to spend some time with my wife and kids before I do. I know I'm gonna get some time out of this wreck thing, and I really want to see my family and take care of some business before I do."

Callo was sure the law was not watching his house or following his wife. They just didn't have the man power for that.

"So what do you have in mind, Arlie? How much time do you need?"

"I need a couple of days. If you could keep them off me for a couple of days, I give you my word that I'll give you the information I have and then I'll turn myself in. I'll even turn myself in to you if you want me to," Arlie said.

"Well, I'm sure I can do that, but here's the way it's gonna have to work. You give me the information you got now. I'll keep them off you, and you turn yourself in at the jail in three days. I'll tell you what. I'll show you I got a big heart and give you till Monday. Fair enough?"

"Okay, man. That sounds good to me."

"Let me make sure you understand something though. If you don't keep your end of the bargain and make me look like an ass, I'll drop everything I'm doing and come looking for you. And when I find you, and you know I will, I promise you I'll make sure they put you under the jail."

"Callo, I swear on my kids I'll keep my word. I just want to see my kids man. I don't want them around when I get arrested. Know what I mean?"

"Yeah, I know what you mean. Just so you know what I mean. I'm really a nice guy, but you really don't want to piss me off."

"I swear I won't, man."

"Well, if we got a deal, tell me what you know about this murder case."

Callo was sure he could arrange things since they probably weren't watching for him anyway.

"Okay, here it is. About a year ago I met this woman. You know, my wife didn't know nothin' about it. Anyway, we seen each other a couple of times. One night we was goin' down Frost Bottom Road and when we passed the pull off place, she started talking about this guy that got killed there a couple of years ago. She told me she knew the guy and even dated him for a while. At first I thought she was bullshittin' me. But the more she talked, the more I realized she knew too much. She had to be telling the truth. She said she had a friend named Linda. She's the sister of the guy that is supposed to have killed this guy. She said that this Linda told her that her brother, his name is Eddie, bragged about how he killed this guy and got away with it."

Callo was listening intently and taking notes as fast as he could. Arlie was right. This was good information.

"She said this guy Eddie is real mean. I guess he killed him because he was fooling around with his old lady. I don't know if this part is true or not but she told me he even took a lie detector test and beat it. That's about all I know. Do you think it

140

will help, Callo?"

"Every little bit helps, Arlie. What's this woman's name and where can I find her?" Callo asked.

"You're not going to tell her you got this from me are you?"

"No, don't worry about that. I wouldn't get much information if word got out that I told where it came from," "Okay then. Her name is Pansey Bell. She lives down on Spring Street in River City. In fact she lives only a few houses from Eddie and his family."

Callo knew Pansey and a couple of her brothers. He knew she liked to party and that she had been arrested, but not for anything serious. He remembered hearing that a couple of years ago her husband was convicted of stabbing one of her brothers to death in another county. He was serving a life sentence, but Pansey always maintained that someone else did it.

"Okay, Arlie, sounds like we got a deal. Give me till morning to get things taken care of for you. Then you can be with your family till Monday. That's when you'll report to the jail. Right?"

"Yeah, right, Callo. I'll be there. I'm tired of looking over my shoulder anyway. I know it's just a matter of time before they'll get me anyway. I really appreciate it."

"Just don't let me down."

"Don't worry. I won't."

"Hey, before you go, let me ask you another question."

"What's that?"

"How come you didn't give this information to the law before now?"

"Shit, Callo. I wouldn't give that outfit a damn thing. They were bigger crooks than I am. I was gonna talk to Danny Bonet once, but I didn't think I could trust him either. That sorry sheriff is right where he belongs."

"I understand," Callo said.

He sat there a few minutes letting the information sink in. He had a good feeling. He hoped that this was the major break in the case he was looking for. He couldn't wait to talk to Pansey Bell himself and see where it went from there. He was looking forward to talking to Louis in the morning too.

"Well, what do you think about the case? You got a theory yet?" Louis asked.

"Not really. Thought I'd wait till I heard yours." Callo knew Louis would be leaning toward Stinner and the Klan connection but was anxious to tell him about the information he received from Arlie Justice the night before. A good investigator knew he had to keep an open mind. As far as he was concerned, although the case was four years old, it was still early in the investigation.

"One thing I thought we could do, Louis is take a ride over to the university and talk with Doctor Bass. I'd like to look at whatever he has and maybe photograph it too," Callo said.

Callo settled in behind one of the desks and asked Louis about his thoughts.

"You know me and Danny worked pretty hard on this case for a while, but to tell you the truth after we ran out of leads we had to move on to other things. The chief didn't like the idea of working on a county case with Collier either. Then Danny left the sheriff's department and came back undercover for the feds. Boy, that was a real piece of work. Anyway, we looked at a guy named Eddie Hooks from River City. We ran him on the poly and he showed deception on only one relevant question. Then I heard some talk on the street and got interested in a guy named Stinner, who was in the Klan. I never could get anywhere with it, but I just had one of those gut feelings about him. If you know what I mean."

"Oh yeah. I sure do. I don't think we can eliminate anybody at this point, but I have to tell you about a call I got last night from a guy that needed a favor."

They spent the next hour tossing ideas around and Callo filled him in on the information about Eddie Hooks.

Callo placed a call to Doctor Bass and was pleased to learn he had some free time if they came right over. Callo was excited to be working a case with Doctor Bass. Over the years he also had attended some homicide and criminal investigation classes in which Doctor Bass was a guest instructor. He admired his work very much.

When they walked into his office under the football stadium, Doctor Bass was genuinely pleased to see them. He was equally pleased that the Keller case had been reopened.

"Doctor Bass, it's good to see you again," Callo said.

"I can't tell you how happy I am that this case has been reopened. I've reviewed my file on it and have laid out everything I have for you to look at."

"I appreciate that. Can we take some photographs of the skull?"

"By all means. Do whatever you think is necessary," Bass said. "As I was getting these things out for you I remembered there was something I intended to do, but since there was no activity on the case until now, I simply put it off. I'm going to send off some fibers from the shirt we found. There were some areas in the material that I just don't believe were caused by animals. There were rips in the shirt down near the hem line that looked to me to be different than those made by animals. I'm going to have the lab compare the damaged fibers to test fibers and try to determine how these cuts in the shirt were made," Bass explained.

"Are you saying you think the shirt may have been cut by a knife, Doctor Bass?"

"I'm saying that's a possibility. I would just feel better if I make that determination. We know this gentleman was shot twice in the head, but that doesn't mean he may not have been cut or stabbed by his assailant also."

"That brings up a question I wanted to ask you, Doctor Bass," Callo said. "As I looked at the photo that was taken when the skull was found in the woods by hunters, I thought about some sharp defense attorney suggesting to a jury down the road that someone may have shot into this skull after it became skeletal. Do you know what I mean? If I can, I'd like to eliminate the possibility that some kook used it for target practice."

"That's an excellent question, Lieutenant. But let me assure you I can testify with certainty that the injuries to the skull were done when this subject was in fact very much alive. There is no question in my mind that those gunshot wounds were the cause of death here," Bass said.

On the way back to the office Louis told Callo he would be out-of-touch for the next couple of weeks. He had planned, and his family was looking forward to, his well deserved vacation. He hated to leave the case again, but he didn't have a choice.

Callo was in deep thought on the drive back. He was thinking about locating Pansey Bell and how to approach the interview with her. He had to be sure he didn't put her in jeopardy. He had to find a safe out-of-the-way place to talk to her. He couldn't take the chance of someone seeing her at his office in the courthouse.

He was also thinking about the feeling that came over him as he came face to face with what was left of Jack Keller in Bass's office. He felt a little foolish when he realized that he found himself actually talking to the skull as it was perched on the table for him to photograph. He remembered

145

saying, "I'm going to find the person who did this to you Jack."

He knew that when he tried to fall asleep that night all he would see when he closed his eyes was the ghostly stare from Jack Keller's skull.

Chapter 10

Leg Work and Interviews

Anthony Callo was consumed by the Keller case, working early days and late nights. The time and effort was paying off and progress was being made. His interviews with people who knew Keller gave him an insight into Keller's life. He told one of the other detectives once that it was almost eerie to know someone so well even though he never met him.

As he began to focus on those closest to Keller, he began to strengthen his theory about the motive. He became more and more convinced the murder was not a drug deal that went bad or a hit because of a bad debt. He was convinced that the motive was as old as the time when there were only two of one sex and one of the other sex on this earth. Jealously.

Shirley Morrison Hooks had been divorced from Eddie Hooks for nearly two years when Callo located her living back in Oak Ridge. He really didn't know what to expect when he knocked on the door of Shirley's duplex apartment. He had only seen a photograph of her taken when she was fifteen years old. When she answered the door, he was surprised to see such a beautiful woman. His first impression was that she was plainly pretty and very country. He knew she had a tough time growing up and was glad to see that she seemed to have survived the early years and her relationship with Eddie Hooks.

"What do you want? Am I in some kind of trouble?" her voice trembled a little.

"No. No. You're not in any trouble, and I'm sorry if I startled you. I just wanted to talk to you about an investigation I'm conducting concerning the murder of a man named Jack Keller."

She seemed to immediately withdraw. He could almost feel her fill with anxiety. He knew he had to find a way to make her relax.

"Shirley, I need your help with this case. I just need you to relax and don't worry about anything. I'm not here to get you involved in something you don't want to be involved in. But this case is long overdue in being solved, and I feel you can help me. I think you may have some information that could be vital to my investigation. It's very important that you be completely honest with me. Jack's family has a right to know what happened to him and see the person who killed him brought to justice. Can I count on you?"

"Come in and have a seat. I really don't like talking about this. It brings back some bad memories. I'd just as soon not relive that part of my life," she said. "I'm really doing good now. I've got a good job, and Eddie has finally stopped bothering me."

"Honey, I give you my word that talking to me is not going to cause you any problems with Eddie or anyone else. Jack didn't deserve to die like he did, and he doesn't deserve for this case to go unsolved. Who knows, maybe the Lord has a way of letting him know you helped bring his killers to justice."

Shirley began to cry and Callo sat next to her on the couch. "Shirley, it's going to be over soon. Then you can really put this episode of your life behind you."

"Let me show you something," she said as she got up and walked over to the bedroom. Callo followed and stood in the doorway as she went to the dresser and picked up a framed photograph. It was Jack Keller. "I really loved him. If it wasn't for me he wouldn't have got killed." She began to cry again.

Callo was sure if she opened up she could provide important information.

"You can prove you loved him. Now's your chance. Let's sit down and you can tell me what makes you feel that way. Okay?"

149

Shirley walked back to the couch still clutching the picture of Jack in her arms.

"Why don't you start by telling me how you first met."

"I met him when I was about fifteen and started seeing him pretty regular. I went lots of places with him because he really treated me good. He asked me lots of times to marry him, but I kept telling him no. I just didn't think deep in my heart that he really wanted to do that. You know. Get tied down. So I kept telling him no. Then I totally screwed up and got with Eddie and married him."

"Did you still see Jack after you married Eddie?"

"Yeah. Eddie treated me real bad. He would beat me all the time and make me feel real cheap."

"Did Eddie find out you were still seeing Jack?"

"Oh, yeah. He was real jealous of Jack and other guys I dated before I married him. One time he was drunk and we drove to the street where Jack lived. Eddie was talking crazy and worked himself up. He messed up my hair and when I fixed it back, Eddie said I was fixin' it back for Jack. He pulled over to the side of the road and started beating me pretty bad. I got a bloody nose and a black eye from that beating. Anyway, he started driving again and we pulled up in front of Jack's house and Eddie pulled me out of the truck and dragged me up to his door. He banged on the door and I saw Jack inside.

He didn't open it. Eddie was yelling for him to open the door. I was telling him not to. There was no telling what Eddie'd do when he got drunk." She started drifting off in thought.

"What happened then, Shirley?" Callo said to get her back on track.

"Jack told him he was going to call the police. I got off the porch and started running away. I hid across the street under some bushes and saw Eddie break the glass in the door. Him and Jack got into a fight, and I saw Eddie knock him down the steps and off the porch."

Callo was listening with interest. Shirley was right on target for his motive. Now that she was started she didn't want to stop until she told it all.

"Eddie was always talking about killing people. He told me one time that he killed an old lady by sticking his you- know- what down her throat. I don't know if it's true or if he just told me these things to scare me. He told me once that he killed his grandmother by hitting her in the head with a stick of firewood. Nobody ever did anything about him 'cause they were all scared of him. Even the police. He really is crazy."

"Did you notice anything different about the way he acted after Jack came up missing?"

"Yeah. He was acting real strange there for a while. He used to take me to the pull-off place off Frost Bottom into the woods. He would beat me and force me to have sex with him. When I heard that's where they found Jack's body, I really freaked out. One time I remember that Eddie was saying Jack's name in his sleep. He kept saying I'll kill you. I'll kill you."

"Did you think he was talking about Jack?"

"Shit, yeah! I knew that's who he was talking about."

"How did you know that?"

"Just by the things he was saying."

"Like what kind of things was he saying?"

"Well, like one time we was driving down the road and Eddie looked like he was crying. I ain't never seen him cry 'bout nothin'. But this time he was. He was saying he didn't mean to do it. When I asked him what he was talking about, he got real mad and told me to shut up or I'd get the same thing Jack got. He told me, I don't know how many times, that if he caught me with anybody else they would get what Jack got too."

"Shirley, did Eddie ever tell you straight up that he killed Jack?"

"No. But I know in my heart that he did," she said.

"I know this has been hard for you, but you have given me some real good information, Shirley. I appreciate you talking to me."

"If you can get the truth out of his brothers, they could tell you all about it I'm sure."

"What makes you say that?"

"Cause Eddie never done nothin' by himself. He could never have got Jack to go into the woods alone with him. Not by himself."

Callo was pleased with the way the

interview went. He felt even more sure he was on the right track, but he knew he had a long way to go. He felt he developed a good rapport with Shirley and was glad because he was sure he would be talking to her again.

It was still early in the day. He decided to drive down to River City and drop by Pansey Bell's house. He was having a good day and hoped she would keep it going that way.

"Is Pansey home?" Callo asked the elderly woman that answered the door.

"Yeah, she's home. You the law?"

"Yes, Ma'am. But she's not in any trouble. I just want to talk to her for a minute."

"Well, just wait there and I'll get her."

"Tell her it's Callo," he said as she closed the door in his face.

"Callo, I can't believe you come to my house and me lookin' like I do," Pansey said as she came bouncing down the porch steps, her hair full of rollers and covered with a towel.

"Whatta ya want from me, Callo? I ain't done nothin' wrong."

Pansey was just joking but she got serious when he told her he was investigating the Keller case.

"Shit, if you want to talk to me about that we need to go somewheres else," she said.

"Okay. Get in the car. We can drive up to the overlook at the dam."

"I ain't goin' nowhere with you and me lookin' like this. Let me go inside and fix myself up

153

a little. Then we can go."

"Okay, but hurry up."

During the drive Pansey and Callo traded small talk. When he got to the overlook, he got down to business.

"Pansey, I've known you for some time now, and you've never lied to me. It's really important that you tell me the truth now. I picked up some talk recently that leads me to believe you might know something I'd be interested in."

Pansey knew that Callo was serious and that he must know something or he wouldn't be there. She knew better than to play games with him, especially on a murder case.

"Okay. I'll tell you what I know but you gotta give me your word that you ain't gonna get me in trouble with certain people. If you know what I mean," she said. "I'd sure like to know how you find out about all this shit."

"I keep my ear to the ground."

"Well, you must. I just hope you keepin' your ear to the ground ain't gonna get me killed."

"I ain't gonna get you killed. Now why don't you start from the beginning and tell me about Jack. And don't leave anything out."

"Okay. Well, you must know that I dated Jack for a while. He was really a nice guy. He had some strange ideas about sex though. But you know me, Callo. That was fine with me," she laughed.

"You mean he liked to take pictures?" Callo said.

"Boy, you really do know some things.

154

Don't you Callo? Oh my God! You don't have any of those pictures of me. Do you?" she said as she buried her face in both her hands.

Callo never did answer. He just gave her one of his looks. He figured, what the hell, let her think whatever she wanted.

"Anyway, me and Jack talked a lot. He told me he was having a lot of trouble with Eddie and his brothers. He said they came to his house once and beat the shit out of him."

"Did he tell you why?"

"Yeah, because he was seeing Eddie's old lady."

"Shirley?"

"Yeah, Shirley."

"Anyway, Linda, that's Eddie's sister, she's one of my best friends. She told me that Eddie killed Jack. She told me that one time the law picked Eddie up for questioning and gave him a lie detectors test. She said that her other brother Darrell had a picture of Jack and he showed it to her. He told her that Eddie did it. She said she asked him how he knew and he told her 'cause he was there when he did it."

"Why didn't you tell her she had to tell the law?"

"I did. She told me I was crazy. She said if she did and Eddie ever found out he would kill her too. She said he was treating everybody in the family real bad. I'll tell you what, Eddie really is crazy. I mean it."

"Is there anything else you can think of?"

155

"The only thing I can think of, is that if he ever found out I told you this, he'd kill me too."

"If I need to talk to you again I'll call you first and we can meet some place," Callo said.

"Yeah, and you better make it after dark. I don't want nobody seeing me with you. Don't get me wrong Callo. You're a pretty cool guy. But people could get hurt after talking to you about this shit."

Callo started the car and headed back toward River City. He glanced over at Pansey who seemed to be in deep thought.

"Is there something else?"

"There is one thing. I'm pretty sure I can find out where Eddie got the gun that he shot Jack with."

"Look at me." Callo stopped the car in the middle of the road. "Do you *think* you know you can find out, or do you already know?"

"There's one thing I need to check out first before I say anything. When I do, I promise I'll call you."

He didn't want to push it right now. He wanted to keep Pansey comfortable with him. "Okay, that's fair enough." He gave her one of his cards and wrote his home number on it.

"You did the right thing. Eddie needs to be put away."

"Yeah, well, all I can say is that you're going to owe me a big one." She started laughing. "Eddie's been mean to his whole family for a long time. I remember he used to beat his brothers and sisters just because he could."

He didn't waste any time when he dropped her off. He pulled over at the end of her driveway and she jumped out and ran into the house.

The next morning Callo went into the sheriff's office and filled him in on the latest developments. Branson was pleased to see the progress being made in the case. He reminded Callo again how important it was, and how much it would mean to solve this case. He told him to use anybody he needed to help him.

"I'll tell you what, Sheriff. As long as things are going so good, I'd just as soon go it alone. I think I might scare off some of the people I've been dealing with if I brought someone else into the case now."

"Well, it sounds real good. You do it the way you want to. Just keep me informed, Jake. And get me some results."

Callo was sitting at his desk catching up on his case file notes when the phone rang.

"Callo, this is Charlie Roberts at the Attorney General's office in Roane County."

"Hey, Charlie. I haven't heard from you in a while. What can I do for you?"

"Well, I just might be able to do something for you for a change. I picked up some information on the case where they found the skeleton in Frost Bottom. I though I'd pass it along to you. It might be nothing, but then again it might mean something to you."

Charlie told Callo he picked up some

information from an informant in his county that Keller was roughed up by a couple of guys and stabbed before he was shot.

Callo was excited about the information. Another piece of the puzzle was fitting in. It would be great if the rips in the shirt Doctor Bass sent to the lab were proven to be caused by a knife.

Callo remembered that Pansey Bell told him she always felt Darrell Hooks was the one that stabbed her brother to death. Maybe he did.

Chapter 11

The Surprise Witness

Dawn Marie Anderson was seventeen, almost eighteen years old. The fact that she was still a juvenile meant that one or both of her parents had to be present when he talked to her. As Callo drove to Batley Road he hoped he would find everyone at home that needed to be there. He was sure it wouldn't take long to find out where he could find Wanda Morrison. The thought crossed his mind that if it didn't take too long, he would actually call it a day early for a change.

When he knocked on the door of the falling-down shack, he heard someone yell from inside the house. Just then a female went running through the back yard. He realized she went out the window, and someone was yelling for her to come back into the house.

Callo ran after her as fast as he could, jumping over piles of junk in the yard. On his heels was Mrs. Anderson who kept yelling, "Don't hurt her!"

Callo caught her at the edge of the woods, and grabbed her by the arm. He was glad she spoke first because he was breathing so heavily and gasping for air, that he needed a second to catch his breath before any words could come out.

"I ain't goin' with you," she yelled. "I ain't done nothing wrong, and I ain't goin' with you."

"Please don't hurt her!" Mrs. Anderson said excitedly.

"I'm not going to hurt anyone," Callo said. "I just want to talk to her."

"Just who are you, Mister?" Mrs. Anderson asked.

"He's the law, Mama," Dawn said.

"Yeah. I'm the law, but I ain't here to arrest you, honey. I just want to ask you a few questions."

Callo officially identified himself as they walked back to the house. He was still breathing heavily.

"Boy, I didn't realize how out of shape I was," Callo said jokingly.

"Well, come in and have a seat, Mr. Callo. I'll get you a drink of water," Mrs. Anderson said.

"Thank you, Ma'am. I think I'll stand. If I sit down, I might not be able to get back up." The truth was the house was pretty nasty. The couch was black with filth, and he was sure it was crawling with fleas from the dog that was curled up on it.

"What do you want to ask me about?" Dawn asked.

"I'm investigating an old murder case, and I talked to Shirley Morrison the other day. She told me you might be able to tell me where I could find her sister Wanda. She said you keep in touch with her."

"Wanda ain't never killed nobody. What murder case are you talking about?"

"I know Wanda didn't kill anybody. I just need to talk to her."

"What murder case is it?" she asked again.

"It's the one where a guy named Jack Keller was killed down in the bottom a few years ago. Do you remember hearing about it?"

Callo wasn't prepared for what happened next. Dawn let out a gasp and covered her mouth with both hands. "Oh my God!" she said.

"What's wrong, Dawn?"

"How'd you know I was there?"

"Well..." Callo wasn't sure what she just said.

"How'd you find out I was there?" she repeated.

"What do you mean, you were there?" Callo said in disbelief.

"I mean I was there."

"There. Where? When?" Callo couldn't comprehend what she was trying to say.

"I was there when that guy got killed. You

mean you didn't know that?"

"No. I didn't know that. I just came here to ask you if you knew where I could find Wanda."

"I never said nothin' 'cause I was scared he would kill me too."

"Who?"

"Eddie," she said.

"Eddie Hooks?"

"Yeah."

Callo could tell she was frightened. He needed to keep her calm, but couldn't wait to hear what she had to say. One thing he had to do was try not to get too excited himself. He couldn't believe that he just might have stumbled onto an actual eye witness to the Keller murder. He wanted to make sure he didn't scare her out of telling her story.

"Listen, Dawn. I'm not going to let anyone hurt you. I give you my word on that. In fact, what we need to do is go to my office and talk. I don't want anyone to see my car parked here at your house. We'll take your mother with us. Is that okay?"

"I guess so," she said as she looked up at her mother for support.

During the trip back to the office with Dawn and her mother, Callo kept reassuring them of the importance of Dawn telling the truth. Dawn had been in some trouble as a juvenile, but this matter was much more serious than she or her mother might imagine. He also assured them again that her safety would be his highest priority.

When they arrived at his office, Callo called

the dispatcher and told her not to send him any calls until he called her back. He was on the verge of getting the most important evidence ever obtained in this case. He didn't want his attention diverted during the interview. In fact he was already thinking that if Dawn provided what he thought she would, he might be able to obtain arrest warrants in the case. He knew, however, he would have to check out the information first and talk with the D.A. Since Dawn had already stated that she was there, he didn't want to take any chance in case she was actually involved.

"Dawn, I want you to understand that I need to read you your rights. Don't get nervous, this is standard procedure. It doesn't mean you're under arrest or anything like that. It's just something I have to do. After all, you already told me you were present when a murder was committed. Do you understand what I'm saying?"

"Yeah, I guess so."

Callo read her a statement of her rights and she signed a waiver, agreeing to talk to him without a lawyer present. Her mother was present and witnessed the statement.

"Okay, Dawn. I think the best thing we can do is just start from the beginning. Tell me how you know Eddie Hooks, and then we'll get into the other things," Callo said.

"Well, a long time ago I dated Eddie. I know he was a lot older than me, but I was kinda wild back then. Anyway, I dated him for about a year and four months."

163

"About how old were you when you dated him?"

"I guess I was about thirteen," she said. "Eddie was married to Shirley at the time, but she left him a lot and fooled around. Wanda told me that Shirley was messing around with a guy named Jack so I didn't think it was so bad for me to see Eddie."

"Did Wanda tell you that Eddie knew for sure that Shirley was seeing Jack?"

"Oh yeah. She told me that. She also told me that Eddie didn't like Jack. Actually, Eddie told me that himself. He told me that him and his brothers went to Jack's house and was gonna beat him up."

"Okay, tell me what you know about Jack getting killed. You told me you were there. What's that all about?" Callo was holding his breath in anticipation of what she was going to disclose.

"Well, one day I was riding around with Eddie and his brothers, Jimmy and Darrell. Eddie wanted to get some beer, so we went to Hilltop Market in Oak Ridge. Eddie and Jimmy went inside. A few minutes later they came out with this guy. He got in the back seat with Darrell. They introduced him to me as Jack. I seen him around before and I thought then that this was the guy that Shirley was messin'' around with. I thought it was kinda funny. Him coming with us."

"How did Jack seem to act?"

"Well, he didn't seem to be very happy to be there. I don't know. I guess you could say he was actin' like he was kinda worried."

"Okay, go on." Callo was writing as fast as he could. He didn't want to miss a word she was saying.

"Anyway, he got in the back seat, and we was riding around. We took a lot of back roads. We went down Beercan Hollar, then to Smith Road, to Batley, then Dutch Valley, and Frost Bottom. We pulled over at the wide spot. You know, where everybody parks."

"Yeah, I know the place you're talking about."

"We sat there for a few minutes talking and listening to the radio when Eddie says, 'Let's take a walk.' I started to get out of the car and he pulled me back in and said, 'No. You stay in the car.' Him and Jack and Jimmy and Darrell got out and they started over the bank into the woods. Jack didn't want to go, but they were kinda pushing him. I sat in the car and listened to the radio."

"Were you drinking beer too?"

"No. I never did like the taste of beer. I wasn't drinking anything except a pop. Anyway, it seemed like they were gone for a long time when I heard what I thought was a gun shot. I know what they sound like 'cause Daddy is always shootin' rats at the house. Anyway, a few seconds later, I heard another shot. A couple of minutes later here come Eddie and his brothers back to the car. Eddie had a strange look on his face. I never seen him look like that. I asked him where Jack was, and he looked at me real funny and said I better shut up and stop askin' questions or I'd get the same thing Jack got. I was real scared." Fear returned in her face as she recalled the events and relived the murder of Jack Keller.

"Why were you scared, Dawn? What did you think happened to Jack?"

"Well, shit, man. It didn't take no genius to figure out they killed him. I heard the shots, and I knew Eddie had a pistol."

"How did you know he had a pistol?"

"He showed it to me once. He always carried it. He said he needed it in case somebody started messin' with him."

"What did it look like? Do you remember?"

"It just looked like a small pistol is all I know. It was real small and he kept it in his pocket."

"What about Jimmy and Darrell? What were they doing?"

"They just got in the back seat and never said nothin'."

"What happened then, honey?"

"We left the pull-off and drove back to the Hilltop Market. He told Jimmy and Darrell to drive Jack's car somewhere, and make sure they wipe off all their fingerprints. Me and Eddie went back to his house and went into the basement. That's where we always went."

"Was Eddie saying anything?"

"He didn't say a word. He just sat there with this strange look on his face. He acted like he was in another world. Then he drove me home."

"When did you see Eddie again after that?"

"The next morning. He came by my house and picked me up. I really didn't want to go with him, but you didn't tell Eddie no. If you know what I mean."

"Where did you go?"

"He said he wanted to take a ride. We drove around for a while, and then we went to the same pull-off place on Frost Bottom. We just sat there in the car for a while. Then Eddie got out and went into the woods. He was only gone a few minutes. When he got back in the car he said, 'Remember that guy Jack?' I said yeah. He said, 'Well, I killed him.' I asked him why and he just said, 'Lets just call it mountain revenge baby. That son-of-a-bitch won't be fuckin' nobody else's old lady I'll tell you that.'

Callo was so excited he could hardly keep his emotions from showing. He knew he had what he needed to bring the case to a close.

"Is there anything else that you remember, Dawn?"

"Oh yeah, Eddie told me that Jimmy and Darrell were pushing him around, and Darrell pulled a knife and told him he was going to cut his...thing off for messin' with his brother's wife. Eddie said Darrell cut him and then he shot him close up in the head. Man, I didn't know what to think He also said when he dropped Jimmy and Darrell off at the Hilltop, they took Jack's car and parked it near the Grove Center movie and left it."

"Dawn. Look at me, honey. Do you swear

167

that everything you just told me is the truth?"

"Yes, sir. It's the truth. Every bit of it. I never told nothin' before because he told me if I ever told anything about it he would kill me and my little sister, my Mama, and Daddy. I didn't see him much after that 'cause I got in some trouble and was sent off to a foster home in Sevierville. Wanda was at the same place with me for a while."

"You did real good, Dawn. I believe what you told me today is the truth. Now what I want you to know is there might come a time when you'll have to go to court and testify to this. You know. In a trial," Callo said.

"That's okay. I ain't scared of Eddie no more. He did a bad thing and he needs to pay for it. I'll go to court and swear to everything I just told you 'cause it's the truth."

Callo typed the information onto a statement and Dawn and her mother read and signed it. Then he called the dispatch and arranged for a deputy in an unmarked car to drive them home. He wanted to let the sheriff know what he had.

As Dawn was leaving the office, she turned to Callo and said, "I'm sorry I didn't tell sooner. And I'm sorry I ran from you this morning."

Callo smiled at her and said, "That's okay, honey. I needed some exercise anyway."

As soon as they left the office Callo picked up the phone and dialed the sheriff's extension. "Sheriff, I need to come up and see you right away. It's important."

"Sure, Jake. Come on up."

Callo was about to bust when he walked into Branson's office and shut the door behind him.

"What's up, Jake?"

"I got what I need to make arrests in the Keller case!"

"You're kidding."

"Nope. My star witness just left my office."

"Fill me in."

"You won't believe this. I went to see this girl to see if she could tell me where I could find someone else, and out of the blue she tells me she was there."

"Whatta ya mean she was there?"

"That's exactly what I said, Sheriff. Anyway, after I chased her all over Hell and half of Georgia, she tells me she was present when Jack was killed. She told me the whole story about how it happened and who did it. She gave me details that she could not have known unless she was there. She was actually there when they did it. Can you believe this?"

"Well, Goddamnit, Jake! Who did it? Don't keep me in suspense like this."

"Eddie Hooks and his two brothers. All I have to do is check out a couple of things and I'll be able to take warrants for them."

"This is great. Do you think you'll have a good case. You think her story will hold up? You know it's one thing to solve it, but we'd look pretty stupid if we made a big thing about solving it and then we didn't get a conviction," Branson said.

"Oh, yeah. I agree. I'm going to run it by

the assistant D.A. and see what she thinks first. But I got to tell you I feel real good about it, Sheriff."

"Boy, this is really great. We can make some progress with this you know," Branson said. "I had a feeling if anyone could do it, you could. Just keep me informed, and before we make any arrests we need to get together and come up with a plan for the press release and all that." Branson was thinking like a politician now, and Callo was walking on air.

"Sure thing, Sheriff. I'll let you know what the D.A. says."

Callo was elated. As far as he was concerned the, case was solved. He just needed to finish up his case file, check on a few more things, and write the affidavits for the warrants.

Taking a few minutes to relax, he sat at his desk thinking about the impact solving this case was going to have on his career in law enforcement. He was excited about the idea of going on to the next unsolved murder case.

He thought about Danny Bonet and how he had it right all along. Danny only needed to catch a couple of lucky breaks and everything would have been different.

Callo knew the warrants would have to contain the names and statements of the witnesses so he would be able to establish the probable cause needed for the arrests.

If he took the case directly to the grand jury, he could testify to the information in secret, but the grand jury wasn't scheduled to meet for another three weeks. There was no way he would be able to sit on this that long. He couldn't afford to have word leak out about his star witness. Getting her killed would really be a disaster. He knew without her testimony, he wouldn't have much of a case.

Chapter 12

Confessions

The next morning Callo rushed into the District Attorney's office and laid out his case to assistant D.A. Joan Hickman. She was a good prosecutor who knew what she wanted in a case. She was not shy when it came to telling an officer that the case needed more work before she would take it to the grand jury or let the officer take arrest warrants.

There were some officers who didn't like her, but Callo knew she was so insistent because she didn't like to lose; neither did he. He knew you only get one shot at a conviction. If there was an acquittal, the defendant couldn't be tried again for the same crime. Callo was pleased with the reaction he got from Joan.

"Okay, here's what I think you should do," she said. "Make sure you check out every aspect of Dawn Anderson's background. The case would hinge on her testimony. Make sure there are no problems in her past concerning her integrity. I'm not going to be too concerned if she didn't go to school or listen to her parents. I just don't want any surprises when I have her on the stand and the defense gets a shot at her."

"Well, let me ask you this, Joan. If Dawn checks out okay, can I go with it?"

"I'd like to have something on the gun. But I think the statement of the Anderson girl is pretty strong. See what else you can come up with and I'll give it a try. After all, the case is pretty old. We really don't have a lot to lose," she said.

When Callo returned to his office, there was a message stuck to his phone for him to call Pansey Bell right away. The note said it was urgent.

"Hey, Pansey, this is Callo. What's goin' on, girl?"

"I'm glad you called me back I got you some information about the gun Eddie had."

"Man, your timing is terrific," Callo said.

"Whatta ya mean by that?"

"Nothing. Just tell me what you got."

"I found out that before Jack got killed, Eddie and one of his brothers tried to break in on this old man down in the bottom. The old guy was supposed to have a lot of money in his house. Anyway, the old guy pulled a gun on them. Well, Eddie just up and took it away from him and then beat the shit out of him."

"Do you know what kind of gun it was?"

"Yeah. I was told it was a small automatic pistol. I think it was a .32. I think you guys call them a Saturday night special," Pansey laughed.

"Do you know what happened to the gun?"

"Now I ain't got no idea about that. I just know Eddie was supposed to have took this gun from the old man, and it was the same gun he killed Jack with. That's all I know."

"This is great. You did real good."

"Yeah, you might just have to deputize me. I'll show you guys how it's done." she laughed again.

"Well, just as long as I'm the one that gets to pin on your badge," Callo joked.

"Yeah. You'd like that wouldn't you, Callo. Naw. I'm just kiddin'. I just got to thinkin' about Jack and what you said. He really didn't deserve to get killed like he did. And there's the other reason I'd like to see them get it."

"What's that?" Callo thought he knew the answer but wanted to let her tell it.

"One of them bastards killed my brother and my old man's in the pen for something he didn't do."

"Maybe we'll see what we can do about that sometime."

Callo got the old man's name and address. He planned to get a statement from him later, but at the moment things were happening very fast. He would really like to have recovered the gun, but if

175

the old man confirms what Pansey told him, it would be some more pretty strong circumstantial evidence.

After spending the rest of the day going over the juvenile records of Dawn Anderson, he found nothing that he thought would hurt his case. He knew he was close now.

He worked late into the night writing the affidavits for the arrest warrants. He had arranged a meeting with the sheriff for the next morning and wanted to have everything ready if the plan called for making the arrests of the Hooks brothers on his warrants right away.

He arrived at the office early the next morning, stopping in the jail kitchen for a cup of coffee before going into the sheriff's office.

"Where you working now?" The sheriff joked. "You must be working for someone else because I never see you around here anymore."

"No, Sheriff, I'm still working for you," Callo said. "As a matter of fact I've been working so hard for you that I'm fixin' to make you look real good."

"Are you saying you're that close to making the arrests in the Keller case?"

"Yes, sir. I've been up half the night writing the warrants and affidavits. All I have to do is get a judge to sign them. But then I got to thinking. Do you think we should make the arrests on warrants instead of going to the grand jury and getting sealed indictments?"

"Have you talked to the D.A. about it?"

"Shit, you know you can't talk to him about anything. So I went in and talked to Joan. She's the one that would be handling the case in court anyway."

"Well, what did she say? Does she think we got a good case?"

"She wanted me to come up with something on the gun. Well, I'll be damned if I didn't go back to my office and there was a message to call Pansey Bell. She told me that Eddie got the gun when he broke in on some old fella to rob him. She said the old timer pulled it on him and Eddie took it away from him. Anyway, she said it was a 32. I'll go down and interview him as soon as I get a chance."

"It sure sounds good to me. I'll tell you something. There's a lot at stake here. If you think you're confident enough to make the arrests, then I'll go along with your feelings. Just don't be wrong."

Callo was well aware that if he couldn't make the charges stick on the Hooks brothers, he and the entire sheriff's department would look pretty incompetent. The sheriff's goal of restoring the confidence in the office was at stake, not to mention maybe even his re-election. There was also the disappointment Jack Keller's parents would endure.

He swallowed hard, took a deep breath, and said, "Sheriff, I think I've got a good case, and I think we should go ahead with the warrants. I need to go find a judge, get them signed, and put a plan together for making the arrests. Then we can let the press know what's going on. That's what I think."

"Okay. If that's what you think we should do, I'll go along with you." Branson read the affidavits and handed them back to Callo. "Go see if you can find a judge. Let's make sure we keep this quiet for now."

"Yeah. I agree. There's nothing to keep these scumbags around. If they got wind of it, they'd probably split."

The judge read each affidavit carefully and signed the warrants for Eddie, Jimmy, and Darrell Hooks, charging them with first degree murder.

Callo tucked the warrants into his coat pocket as he left the judge's chambers and headed back to the sheriff's office. He thought to himself that not so long ago he was looking for more action than he had as chief of police in Norris. Now here he was with a pocket full of warrants for first degree murder and was getting ready to put a plan together to make the arrests. He probably couldn't find more action than that.

"No trouble at all, Sheriff. I've got the warrants in my pocket." Callo was excited. The arrest in this case were long overdue. He was looking forward to making the call to Mr. and Mrs. Keller after the arrests were made.

"How do you think we should go about making the arrests, Jake?"

"I think we should have a meeting with everybody that will take part late tonight and hit the Hooks house real early in the morning. You know. Catch them with sleep in their eyes. Before they know what hit them." Callo was excited. He had been looking forward to this event for some time.

"That sounds good to me," Branson said. "Give me a list of the names of who you want on the raid, and I'll have my secretary contact them for the meeting tonight."

"Okay, Sheriff. I'll bring a list up in a little while."

The mood at the meeting that night was very serious. The officers were made aware that the Hooks brothers could be very dangerous. After all not one of them had ever taken part in the arrest of three murder suspects. The plan called for an officer to leave right after the meeting and be dropped off about a half mile from the house. He would walk down the railroad tracks and find some cover across the street from the house to keep the house under surveillance all night.

When they hit the house about six in the morning, there would be a team of two officers at the back door and a team on each side of the house. Callo and the sheriff would lead four more officers into the house by the front door. They agreed they would knock once and then force their way in.

When Callo laid down to get a few hours sleep, his mind went into overdrive. He went over all the circumstances that he put into the affidavits. He knew the arrests would be a big media event. The local newspapers were sure to keep the case on the front page during every step of the proceedings. He thought also the success of this case would cause even greater pressure to solve the next case. He couldn't afford for anything to go wrong at this stage of the game.

He was apprehensive. What if he missed something about Dawn Anderson, and the defense was able to discredit her on the stand? What if some of the witnesses who supplied much of the circumstantial evidence got cold feet and changed their story? He knew he should have already talked to the old man about the gun, instead of putting it off. He finally drifted off to sleep, only to get up in less than two hours.

Another briefing was held when everyone returned to the sheriff's office at 5:00 A.M. They all put on their bullet proof vests, and headed out for River City. The press would be alerted only after the suspects were in custody.

The caravan approached the house from two directions, turning out their headlights as they rolled into position. The officer that had the house under surveillance told them he thought all the suspects were in the house, but someone spent the night in an old van that was parked in the driveway.

The officers poured out of their cars and scurried to their positions. Sheriff Branson and Callo dashed for the front door. They burst into the house with weapons drawn, yelling orders for everyone to get on the floor. Callo spotted Jimmy on the couch and had him handcuffed before he could even realize what was going on. He was searched and told to just sit there on the couch. "What's going on, man?" he asked. Callo didn't answer. Darrell was dragged out of the attic space,

180

where he had a makeshift bed, and handcuffed.

They brought him over to the couch and sat him next to his brother. Callo stepped out onto the front porch and saw Eddie was being cuffed at the side of the van parked in the yard. He could see Eddie was running his mouth and giving the officers a hard time. He walked up to them and asked what the problem was.

"I want to know what the hell is going on here," Eddie said. "I hope you assholes got a warrant."

"Oh we got a warrant, Eddie. You're under arrest for the murder of Jack Keller," Callo said with a great deal of satisfaction.

"That's a bunch of shit. I ain't killed nobody," he screamed. "I'm gonna sue your ass off, buddy!"

"Well, right now you got bigger problems than thinking about suing me, Eddie. Put him in the car," Callo said.

"You think you're a big shot. Don't you, Callo? Well, you really screwed up this time, 'cause I ain't killed nobody."

Callo went back into the living room of the shack and told the officers to make sure they transport them in separate cars. He also asked the chief of patrol to tell the jailers to make sure they are kept in separate cells. He didn't want them talking to each other until he had a chance to interview them.

"Sheriff. It went pretty good. Don't you think?"

"It went great. It was a good idea to catch them so early," Branson said. "They didn't have any idea what was going on. And the best thing is that nobody got hurt."

Callo was relieved that the arrests were made. Now all he had to do was convict them. With some smooth talking and some luck, that would be a lot easier if he could get one or all of them to confess.

When he arrived at the jail, the press was already waiting. The sheriff made a brief statement and then turned them loose on Callo. He never experienced anything like this. He was careful not to give them too much detail. He knew that since the arrests were made on warrants as opposed to grand jury indictments, there would be a preliminary hearing in about a week. Callo was flying high. He handled the press well, making sure to give credit to all the officers that took part in the arrests.

The judge had pre-set the bonds at two hundred and fifty thousand dollars each, an impossible amount for any of them to come up with. After they were all booked, dressed out in the jail's orange jumpsuits, and put into separate cells, Callo asked the jailer to bring one of them down to his office. He felt thought Darrell was the weakest link and started with him. He had to act quickly so he could get a chance to talk to them before they got a court appointed attorney.

"Come on in here and have a seat, Darrell," Callo said. "I had them bring you down here so I could explain to you what's going on. I want to read you the warrant and make sure you know what your rights are. If you have any questions, I want you to feel free to ask me. I promise I won't lie to you. All I ask is that you don't lie to me either. You understand?"

"Yeah. But all I got to say to you is that I didn't kill nobody," Darrell said.

"Wait a minute, buddy. I want to read you this statement of your rights. It's important to me that you understand what rights you have," Callo said.

After reading the admonition, which he was sure Darrell knew by heart anyway, he got him to sign the document. What he signed his name to was a statement that he understood his rights and agreed to talk to him without a lawyer present.

"Okay, with that out of the way, let me tell you this, Darrell. You're in a lot of trouble here. This ain't no public drunk charge. You're charged with first degree murder. Do you know what that means?" Callo could see that Darrell was scared to death.

"I told you, man, I ain't killed nobody."

"Well, I don't think you did kill Jack Keller. But the way it works in this state is that if you aided and abetted in a murder, the charge is the same as if you pulled the trigger yourself," Callo said. "I know who pulled the trigger. I know that Eddie was the trigger man, and I promise you I'm going to put him in the electric chair. Now, if you don't want to be sitting on his lap when he fries, then you better get your heart right and start telling me what I want

183

to know about your involvement in this case."

Callo was studying Darrell's reaction intently. He saw him swallow hard and sweat was popping out on his forehead. By the time he read him the affidavit in the warrant, especially the part about Dawn Anderson's statement, Darrell was squirming in his chair. Callo knew he was getting close to a confession.

"As you can see, I've got a good case. I just didn't make up this shit. And let me tell you something else. This man, Jack Keller, didn't deserve to have three fucking rednecks drag him into the woods and blow his brains out." Callo was within an inch of Darrell's face and was raising his voice. "I can prove everything I've read to you, and when I do, I'm going to see that the state requests the death penalty, and the three of you get the chair."

Callo had come on strong. Now it was time to change his tone a little and give Darrell a little breathing room.

"What it boils down to, Darrell, is that you control your own destiny. Right here and right now. All you have to do is tell the truth."

"Well, the truth is, either the state kills me or Eddie kills me. So what's the difference?" Darrell said.

Callo knew he had him now. That was pretty a incriminating statement.

"Buddy, let me assure you of one thing. You never have to fear Eddie again. I know how he treats everybody in your family. But I'm telling you, Eddie will never see daylight again," Callo told him. "Now the smart thing for you to do is for you to let him take the rap for a change. Eddie created this problem for you. Don't let him keep using you."

"Jesus Christ. You don't make it easy."

"You didn't make it easy for Jack Keller," Callo said coldly.

"It's like this, man. Eddie's the one who done it. Everything you read me is true. Everything that girl said is the way it happened." Darrell seemed almost relieved.

"You're doing the right thing," Callo said.

"To tell you the truth, this thing has been driving me crazy for a long time. I don't guess it bothers Eddie much 'cause he don't give a shit about nothin'," Darrell said.

"Tell me this. Why did he do it?"

"'Cause of his old lady, man. She was screwing around with this guy and Eddie hated him. I told him she wasn't worth it, and he got real pissed at me. That's why he done it," Darrell said as he hung his head.

"Okay. What I'd like to do is get this all down in the form of a statement. Do you think you can do that for me?"

"I don't write so good. You write it out for me and I'll sign it. If that's okay."

"Yeah, I can do that for you, buddy," Callo said.

Darrell related the facts as Callo compiled a statement almost three pages long. The statement covered the fact that he was not presently under the influence of drugs or alcohol and was not threatened in any way to get him to confess. He read the statement back to Darrell and handed it to him to sign.

Darrell hesitated and said, "There's one more thing, Callo."

"What's that?"

"Eddie told me that the next day he went back to this guy's body and robbed him."

"What do you mean?"

"I mean he went back and took his watch and the money off the dead body the next day. I swear I didn't go with him and I didn't get any of the money. Eddie kept it all."

Callo knew now just how cold blooded Eddie was. He walked over behind Darrell and put his hand on his shoulder and said, "You know you did the right thing. Don't you?"

"Yeah. I guess so," he said as he began to sob.

"Do you think Jimmy will do the right thing, too?" Callo asked.

"Yeah, I know he will. You get him in here and he'll tell you the same thing. To tell you the truth, we talked about this before, me and Jimmy. We done decided that if we ever got caught, we was going to tell about Eddie."

Darrell was right. Jimmy was brought down and gave a statement almost identical to the one Darrell gave Callo. When he called the jail and asked for Eddie, the jailer told him that Eddie didn't have anything to say until he got a lawyer. Callo was pleased. He was sure now that the case against Eddie was as air tight as he could get it. As far as he was concerned, the D.A. could make any deal he wanted with Darrell and Jimmy. He just wanted to make sure he had Eddie between a rock and a hard place. He felt confident that nothing could go wrong

Callo couldn't help feeling a little sorry for Jimmy and Darrell. He had never seen an intimidation of family members like the one Eddie made his family suffer with. Making up his mind that he would help them if he could, he couldn't dwell on it. There will still be a lot of work to do. Making the arrests was only the first step in getting to the final conclusion in this case. The preparation for the hearings and trial, was going to be a big job.

He wanted to pick up the phone and call Mr. and Mrs. Keller, but for some reason, felt it wasn't the right time. There was an uneasy feeling that came over him. Now that he looked back on the events, maybe it all came together easier than he had expected. He wasn't about to look a gift horse in the mouth, but it sure was a stroke of luck, stumbling onto Dawn Anderson. He thought it would be best to let the dust settle for a while before making the call to the Keller family.

Chapter 13

Dalton's Revenge

Callo leaned back in his chair, taking a moment to relax and reflect on the day's events. He closed his eyes for a moment. Everything was so quiet, he almost drifted off to sleep. He was startled by a knock at the open door of his office. It was Avery Givens, the criminal investigator from the District Attorney's office.

"Hey, Jake. Did I catch you at a bad time?"

"No, buddy. It's just been a long day. Come on in," Callo said.

"What's going on? Callo was a little surprised by his visit.

"The D.A. sent me down to see you. I really hate to be the one to do this to you. But he's called a special session of the Grand Jury for late this afternoon, and I've got a subpoena for you," Givins said as he handed him the paper.

"For what case?" Callo asked. Before Givens could answer, the phone rang.

"Jake, can you come up to my office right away?"

"Sure thing, Sheriff. What's going on?"

"We've got some big problems. Some people are here who need to speak with you." Callo was concerned by the tone in the Sheriff's voice.

"I'll be right up," he said.

"What's going on, Avery? What case is this all about?"

"Jake, all I can tell you is that the D.A.'s pissed about the arrests, and he's called a special Grand Jury in the Keller case. I swear that's all I can tell you," Givens said.

"Well, I better go upstairs and see what the Hell's going on here."

When he walked into the Sheriff's office he was shocked to see District Attorney Jim Reynolds in the room. As far as he knew, this was the first time he had been in the Sheriff's office. The relationship between the Sheriff and the D.A. had been strained at best for a long time. They really didn't get along at all.

Also in the office was Tennessee Bureau of Investigation Agent, Mark McBride.

"Jake, come on in and close the door," Branson said.

"What's this all about, Sheriff? Callo asked.

"Well, the District Attorney says we've

arrested the wrong people in the Keller case." The Sheriff really looked angry. But Callo didn't know if he was mad at him or the D.A.

"Bullshit!" Was the only word Callo could think of.

"It's not bullshit, Callo," Reynolds said. "Agent McBride here has a sworn statement from an informant that has passed a polygraph test saying that he was present when the murder was committed by someone other than the Hooks brothers."

Callo was stunned. "Well, I don't know what's going on here, and I don't give a damn what he's got. I've got confessions from Darrell and Jimmy Hooks. They tell the same story that Dawn Anderson tells about Eddie Hooks killing Keller."

"That may be. But the problem is this information is exculpatory. That means I'll have to give it to the defense. There is no way I'd be able to convict anyone in this case with these two conflicting stories. Besides, I'm really pissed about the fact that I didn't even know anything about your investigation. My office had no idea you were going to make arrests in this case," Reynolds said. "I was sitting in a conference where Doctor Bass was speaking and he was showing this skull with a bullet hole in it and says it's an Anderson County case. I was stunned. When he was through, I spoke to him out in the lobby. I really felt like a fool having to have Doctor Bass tell me about a a case in the county that I'm the DA in and I don't know a damn thing about it."

"Now wait a minute," Callo interrupted.

"Joan and I went over this case just the other day, and she said she would go with it."

"She told me she didn't know you were going to take warrants. I had to find out about it through the media. How do you think that makes me look when I don't know a damn thing about a murder case my office will have to prosecute?"

"I'm sorry if things got a little mixed up. There must have been a misunderstanding between me and Joan."

"Joan is not the District Attorney. I am. Besides you never take warrants without my permission."

"Well, I've got a flash for you, Jim. I don't work for you. I work for the Sheriff."

"Now wait a minute. This is not getting us anywhere," Branson said. He could see the faces getting red on both Callo and Reynolds.

"Sheriff, I feel strongly about this case. Eddie Hooks killed Keller and I can prove it," Callo said.

"That might be so," Reynolds said. "But you can't prove it without me. I've called a special session of the Grand Jury for this afternoon and I'm sending McBride in with his information. I'm going to ask them not to indict the Hooks brothers and I want you there."

"Yeah. I've got your invitation in my pocket," Callo said sarcastically.

Callo glanced over at McBride. He thought to himself that he should have been made aware that the T.B.I. was working on the case too.

"Now let me see if I understand this, Jim. You said you're going to ask for a no true bill from the Grand Jury. Right?" Callo said.

"That's right."

"What about the warrants I made the arrests on?"

"I'm going to have Joan go to the Judge in the morning and have them dismissed," Reynolds said.

"That will mean we'll have to cut Eddie and his brothers loose."

"That's right."

"Oh that's great. Have you read those affidavits? I had to put witnesses names in them. How the Hell am I supposed to protect these people when these guys hit the streets?" Callo asked.

"That's your problem."

Callo looked at the sheriff, desperately wanting him to intervene. But he knew the district attorney has the last word. If he chose not to prosecute a case, that's the way it was.

"Holly shit, Sheriff! Are you listening to this? We're gonna have to let these guys out of jail."

"I asked you if you talked to the D.A., Jake," Branson said.

"Jesus, Sheriff. I spoke to Joan, his assistant. It's not my fault that he don't know what the Hell is going on in his own office."

That comment really pissed Reynolds off. He stood up to leave and said, "Listen, you had a choice. I don't. Just make sure you're at the grand

193

jury on time, Callo."

"Oh don't worry. I'll be there. But I want you to know, I'm going to lay out my findings to them."

"That's your decision. But I hope you know, I'm going to tell them not to indict. And that's the way it's going to be."

As Reynolds and McBride were leaving the office, Callo said, "Hey, McBride. When can I get a look at the name and so-called statement of your informant? I think I'm entitled to know who is saying what in this case. Don't you?"

"Yeah, sure. Here's a copy. Read it over. The informant's name is Bill Dalton."

"Bill Dalton!" Callo said in disbelief. "Bill Dalton," he repeated. "You've got to be kidding me."

"No. I'm not kidding you. Right here's his sworn statement."

"Since when do you put any stock in anything Bill Dalton has to say, Jim?" Callo asked. "You know his credibility isn't worth two cents."

"Just be at the grand jury, Callo," Reynolds said without looking back.

"Hey, McBride. One more thing. The suspense is killing me. I've got to know who Dalton says killed Keller."

McBride stepped into the Sheriff's outer office and turned to Callo and said, "He says Danny Bonet killed him."

"Danny Bonet!"

"That's right. Danny Bonet. And just

194

remember this. He gave me a sworn statement and passed a polygraph test," McBride said.

"A sworn statement. I wouldn't believe that son-of-a-bitch if he was standing on a stack of Bibles."

Callo went back into the Sheriff's office. Branson didn't look so good.

"Well, what are we going to do now?" he asked Callo.

"I guess we're going to have to do some damage control. I don't even want to think about what the press is going to do with this," Callo said. He knew that's what the Sheriff was thinking about so he just went ahead and said it.

"Do you think there's anything to what Dalton is saying Jake?"

"Hell no, I don't. I bet I can take this statement apart in no time. Besides I got confessions from two of the brothers. Bill Dalton's the biggest liar I've ever met. The two Hooks brothers sure as Hell ain't going to tell me they killed someone if they didn't do it."

"I agree. But what the Hell are we going to do with Reynolds?"

"Actually, Sheriff. That's not what worries me the most right now. What worries me is that I gave Dawn Anderson and her mother my word that nothing would happen to her. I'm just going to have to find a way to keep it, I've got to make sure that Eddie doesn't find out that Darrell and Jimmy gave me a statement too. Shit, he'll kill them all, for sure."

195

"Jake. I don't have to tell you what this might mean, do I?" the Sheriff said.

"No. You sure don't, Sheriff. But listen. Let's not get too panicky just yet. First, let's see what happens at the grand jury. Then I'll start working on this so-called statement. I'll call McBride tonight and talk to him without the D.A. around."

"Okay. I'm going to work up a press release just in case we have to let these guys out of jail," Branson said. "I'd like to beat Reynolds to the punch so we can put our own spin on it."

"Good idea, Sheriff. Just trust me. I have a feeling everything is going to work out just fine."

"Okay, I'll trust you. But you better be right."

Callo knew by the Sheriff's tone that he meant what he said about being right. There was a lot at stake.

Callo knew he had his work cut out for him. He had to protect Dawn Anderson. He also had to make sure he didn't piss off the D.A. any more than he already had and get him to the point of wanting to prosecute his case.

When he got back to the office, the first call he made was to Danny Bonet.

"Hey, Danny. How's everything going?"

"I'm doin' okay. I heard about the arrest in the Keller case. I figured you were real busy, so I thought I'd call you tonight to tell you what a good job you did."

"Thanks. But a problem has come up."

"What kind of a problem?"

"Let me ask you a question first. What happened when you and Dalton went your separate ways? I mean did he get real pissed off at you?" Callo was going to take a big chance telling Danny that he had become a T.B.I. suspect in the Keller case. He didn't like to interfere in another agency's investigation. But he knew McBride was on the wrong trail. He felt he had to talk to Danny about it to see what the motive for Dalton's lies could be.

"Oh yeah. He got real mad because I wouldn't help him out of some trouble in Knox County. In fact I had a couple of people tell me that Dalton told them that some day he would get even with me. But you know how Dalton is, Jake. He's all mouth. I wasn't too worried about it," Danny said.

"Why? What's going on with Dalton? Has he been saying bad things about me?" Danny laughed.

"You're right about one thing. He's all mouth. But when I tell you what he's been saying, you've got to promise me that you ain't going to go out and whip his ass," Callo said.

"Okay. I won't go out and whip his ass. Now what's he been saying Jake?"

"You won't believe this, but he told Mark McBride with the T.B.I. that you killed Keller and that he was there when it happened."

"You gotta be shittin' me! Don't tell me that McBride believes that bullshit."

"Well, he's a young agent. I'm sure he

197

heard all about you, and he thinks he can get himself a big fish. Know what I mean?"

"That stupid son-of-a-bitch. What an asshole," Danny was getting mad.

"How does this affect your case? I know you got a good case or you never would have made the arrests."

"Well, Reynolds has called a special session of the grand jury, and McBride is going in. He's going to ask them not to indict the Hooks brothers."

"But you've already arrested them. Didn't you?"

"Yeah. I arrested them on warrants. He's going to get the warrants dismissed and I'll have to cut them loose."

"Is that stupid bastard going to try to indict me?"

"No. I'm sure this is all bullshit, Danny. I'm sure it's all politics he's playing with the sheriff. He got pissed because he didn't know anything about my case, and now he wants to make the sheriff look bad. That's all. I really don't think he cares if anybody ever gets indicted for killing Keller."

"Man, you've got yourself a mess. I bet Branson was all over you."

"To tell you the truth Danny, I think he's still in shock. If I can't get this worked out, he is going to look like a horse's ass."

"I really don't care if Branson looks bad, but I really hate it for you. I know you worked your heart out on this one."

"I'm gonna get it all worked out but it's gonna take some time. What I need from you is your word that you ain't gonna let on that you know anything about the T.B.I. investigation. I could probably get in a lot of trouble for telling you about Dalton," Callo said.

"It really pisses me off. Dalton running his mouth with a pack of lies. But, yeah, you've got my word. Just get back to me and let me know what's going on. Okay?"

"I'll get back to you in a couple of days Danny. I'll take care of Dalton."

"Okay, but don't wait too long. Dalton's got to get what's coming to him, and I'd like to be the one that gives it to him."

"Just cool off, Danny. My case is fucked up enough as it is. I don't need you going out and doing anything to make things worse. It's got to be hands off Dalton. You've got to just leave it to me."

"Okay. I'll leave it alone for now."

"Thanks."

"Oh, one more thing, Jake."

"What's that?"

"I hope you know I didn't kill anybody," Danny laughed. "At least not yet."

"Thanks, Danny. I'll be in touch soon," Callo said.

When Callo got upstairs to the grand jury room, McBride was already in there. While he was waiting, he read the statement Dalton gave to the T.B.I. He couldn't believe how leading the questions were. No wonder he passed a polygraph test. After reading the statement he actually felt better because there were things in it that he knew he could prove false without any trouble. He had time to cool down a little. It was so obvious what Dalton had pulled off. He took a young agent and planted a seed. Now he was using what developed to make Danny Bonet's life miserable.

Callo decided that when he went in to testify before the grand jury he would lay out his case against the Hooks brothers, but would go along with a no true bill. He wanted to show them that he was willing to work with the district attorney. He also wanted them to know that he could quickly deal with the T.B.I. informant, and that would make his case against the Hooks brothers even stronger. He also knew that if this other information had come out during a trial, even though it was not true, the brothers may have been acquitted. That would mean they would have gotten away with murder.

McBride came out of the room and told Callo they were ready for him.

"Mark, I've had a chance to look over Dalton's statement. Can I call you this evening and go over a few things with you?" Callo asked.

"Sure. Here's my home number. I'll help you in any way I can. Call me tonight."

"Thanks." Callo thought to himself, what a jerk McBride was. He disliked him more all the time. But he needed to be nice to him, at least until he got this mess straightened out about Danny Bonet.

When he went into the courtroom, he noticed there were a couple of members on the Grand Jury panel that he knew. He stayed with his decision to go along with the D.A.'s request. However, he made the point that he would return as soon as he could prove the other statement worthless. One jury member told him that he had confidence in his abilities and was looking forward to him bringing the case back before them.

When he finished in the Grand Jury, he drove down to talk to Dawn Anderson and her parents. He filled them in on what was going on and told them that the Hooks were going to be released.

"Well, now I hate that those boys might get out of jail, Mister. But I've got my shotgun loaded with double ought buck and I'm telling you right now, if they show their faces 'round here, the funeral home will be packin' their ass with cotton," Mr. Anderson said.

Callo laughed, even though he knew Anderson was dead serious.

"I really don't think they would try anything, but just in case I'm going to have an officer in a patrol car across the street from your house until this thing is worked out," he told them.

"I ain't scared of them no more," Dawn said.

"Well, I hope I'll have them back in jail real soon. This time for good. Here's my home number. If you need anything, you be sure to call me." He gave them his card and headed back to the office. He wanted to read over Dalton's statement again.

When he got home that night, he was totally exhausted. After eating supper, he went into the den and called Agent McBride.

"Jake, all I can tell you is that he passed a polygraph test. Yeah, there are some things that I'm not comfortable with, but he seems like he knows things that no one else should know," McBride said.

"Well, let me ask you this. Did you know that at one time he was a paid informant for Bonet?"

"Yeah, he told me that," McBride said.

"Did he also tell you that he got pissed off at Danny because he wouldn't help him after the dumb ass got arrested in Knox County for shooting at a guy?"

"He told me him and Danny went their separate ways, but didn't give me any details."

"I'll bet you didn't know that when the remains were found, he was on the scene with Danny. In fact he actually helped him take measurements and photographs," Callo said.

"No, I wasn't aware of that," McBride admitted.

"Mark, I've got a photograph of Dalton at the scene holding a note pad."

"Well that could explain how he knows so much detail about it," McBride said.

Callo thought, well maybe McBride isn't as dumb as he thought he was. Then the idea hit him like a bolt of lightning.

"I'll tell you what I'd like to do, Mark. I'd like to get Dalton back to the scene and have him walk us through how he says the murder occurred."

"I don't know if he'll agree to do that," McBride said.

"Jesus Christ, Mark. How would he have a choice? He gave you a statement that he actually took part in this murder. Who the hell is working who? Just tell him he has no choice."

"Okay, I'll set it up, but I can't do it tomorrow. I've got to be in court in another county all day."

"How about Friday?" Callo asked.

"Friday is good for me. I'll get in touch with Bill and have him at the scene at 9:00 o'clock in the morning."

"Mark, I really appreciate your cooperation, and I don't want you to think I'm trying to tell you how to do your job. It's just that I know Dalton a whole lot better than you do. He's a damn liar, and I happen to know that he made statements that he would get even with Danny Bonet for not helping him in Knox County," Callo said.

"Well, when he gets out there, we'll see what he says. He may not be telling the truth. But if he's not, he's a damn good liar," McBride said.

"Oh, he's good all right. After all, that's what the guy does for a living," Callo said. "I'll see you Friday morning down on Frost Bottom."

Callo didn't sleep well that night. He knew he had this one shot at Dalton. He had to hit the bulls-eye. He kept going over Dalton's statement in his mind. If he got Dalton a little shaky, and confronted him on some of his lies, he just might be able to break him down and get the truth out of him.

The next morning Callo found himself driving past the courthouse; almost as in a daze. He realized when he came to a stop he was in the pull-off area on Frost Bottom Road.

He sat in his car for a long time going over in his mind the recent developments in the case. He was missing something; but he had no idea what it was. He thought perhaps if he retraced what he was certain were Jack Keller's last steps, it would come to him.

He got out of the car and walked across the gravel area, down the embankment, deeper into the woods. When he stopped, he realized he was standing at the base of the towering pine tree where Keller took his last breath.

A fear gripped him; just as it must have Keller. Only his fear was not of being killed. He feared that justice might not be served, and those cold-hearted bastards that took Jack Keller's life would never be punished.

"Okay, Jack. Here I am. Now tell me what I'm looking for," he said out loud. "God damnit Jack! What is it?" he shouted.

When he realized he was talking to himself, he felt a little foolish. Turning to walk back up the hill, he took two steps and stopped dead in his tracks. At that moment, he knew what he needed to be looking for. He was absolutely convinced that if he found it, he would be able to discredit Dalton's statement and prove he was a liar.

He scrambled up the bank and raced back to

the office. He had to make arrangements to get his plan in motion.

When he pulled into the parking space behind the jail, the Hooks brothers were leaving the building. He couldn't avoid them. Eddie was the only one that spoke.

"Hey, Callo. I don't know what the Hell's going on, but I told you I didn't kill nobody. Hope you got lots of money, 'cause I'm going to sue you and this county for all I can."

Callo walked up to him and looked him right in the eye. "No, you're not, Eddie. Because I never quit, and this thing is not over yet. I'll be seeing you again real soon. You can count on it."

"Well, we'll just see about that," Eddie said as he was getting into his father's car.

Callo went into the office and called the dispatcher. He asked her to have Deputy Wilder meet him in his office right away. He outlined the plan to him and told him he needed some help. They told no one where they were going or what they were up to. He wasn't sure he would meet with success, but if he did, the result would be impossible for Dalton to lie his way out of. He knew if he found what he was looking for, it would give him the break he needed in Dalton's story and the chance to start taking him apart.

Chapter 14

Anxious Moments

Lieutenant Callo loaded the entire case file into his car and headed for the bottom. On top of the file in his briefcase was the copy of Bill Dalton's statement and a large envelope containing the photographs, including the enlargements he had made from the original photographs taken by Danny Bonet. Wrapped in cotton, inside a small white gift box was what he hoped would be the evidence that would break Bill Dalton's story.

Callo was tired. The events of the day before were taxing, but rewarding. He and Deputy Wilder finished the day with a six hour round trip drive to the State of Tennessee Crime Laboratory in Nashville.

He arrived at the pull-off area on Frost

Bottom Road early. He smoked a half pack of cigarettes, one right after the other, before he saw McBride's car coming up the road. He could see that McBride was driving and that Bill Dalton was on the passenger side of the front seat. The car passed by the pull-off area without stopping. Callo was puzzled. He was certain McBride saw him parked there.

Callo thought to himself it would be nice if Dalton, who says he was present when Keller was killed, couldn't even show them where it happened. No such luck. A couple of minutes later McBride returned and pulled into the gravel area. Dalton didn't get out of the car.

"What's going on, Mark?" Callo asked.

"He says he don't want to do it. He says he's afraid of you."

"Bullshit! He's afraid of the truth. That's what he's afraid of," Callo said as he got out of his car and walked over to Dalton.

"What's the problem, Bill?"

"I don't know if I want to do this."

"Listen. You know I'm the investigating officer in this case. If what you say is true. I'll be behind you one hundred percent." Callo was playing him along; hoping to get Bill to think he believed him too. "I just need you to go over this with us so we have a clear idea of how things went down."

"I don't know, man," Dalton said.

"Look. What have you got to lose? I don't know what kind of deal McBride made you, but you're a pretty smart guy and you gotta know it sure can't hurt to have me on your side too. Right?"

"Yeah. I guess so."

"I've got your statement right here. Let's just go over a few things. Whatta ya say?"

"Well, I'll do it the best as I can remember," he said as he got out of the car.

"Good. That's all we're asking," Callo said as he glanced over at McBride who was no help at all.

"I really don't know where to start."

Callo sensed the he was very nervous; probably because he was afraid this whole thing was going to backfire in his face. Dalton knew Callo well. He knew he was sharp, and would be hard to fool. Dalton didn't have a clue about what Callo knew about the case. He also didn't have any idea what Callo was going to hit him with.

"Just start from the beginning. Tell us how Danny knew this guy Jack Keller. Just relax, Bill. I'm sure it will all come back to you. Don't worry. I'm not going to hurt you." Callo laughed. Dalton didn't.

"Well, like I told McBride. Danny knew Keller from hanging out at the bars in Oak Ridge. Keller played in a band. If I remember right, he played the drums."

"That's right. He did play the drums. See I told you this won't be too hard, and that it would all come back to you." Callo was being very patient and leading him very carefully.

"You're on a roll, Bill. Now go on and tell

209

us how this thing with Keller and Danny came about."

"Well, like I said. Danny knew him from the bars. Danny didn't like him very much. He told me Keller was a ladies man. That's where the problem started."

"Whatta ya mean?"

"Danny was seeing this woman, and Keller was hitting on her."

"Do you remember what her name was?"

"No. I don't remember her name."

That was no surprise to Callo.

"Anyway, Danny picked me up one night and we went to the Smoke House in Oak Ridge. Danny was drinking pretty heavy that night. Well, he asked me to get in a pool game with Keller and kinda get friendly with him. So I did. Later that night he got me on the side and told me to ask Keller if he would drive me home. If he said okay, I was supposed to tell him I lived on Frost Bottom Road."

"Did he agree to take you home?"

"Yeah. He said okay but I had to put some gas in his car."

"What happened then?"

"Danny had told me that when we went down Frost Bottom, and we came to the pull-off area, I was supposed to tell Jack to pull over so I could take a piss."

"And is that what happened?"

"Yeah. Danny was parked there with his lights off. You know. Waiting for us. Anyway, when we stopped, Danny came up to Jack's car and told him to get out. That's when Danny pulled a thirty-two out of his pocket and just shot him in the head."

"Danny shot him just like that? They didn't have any words?" Callo asked.

"No. Danny never said nothing. He just up and shot him. He dropped right in his tracks"

"Then what happened?"

"Shit, I was freaking out. I asked him what the Hell we was going to do now. He told me to grab one of his legs, and he took the other one, and we dragged his body over the bank and rolled it down the ridge."

"So how many times did Danny shoot him?"

"Oh yeah, I almost forgot. Danny went down the hill and shot him again in the head," Dalton said.

"What did you do then?"

"Danny told me to drive Keller's car to Grove Center in Oak Ridge and leave it in the parking lot. He told me to make sure I wipe all my fingerprints off the car. Then he picked me up a little while later."

"Okay, here's what I'd like you to do. Why don't you show us where everybody was standing, and what you all did," Callo said.

"Well, Danny's car was parked right over there, and Keller pulled in right about here someplace," Dalton said.

"Okay, then Danny got out of his car and came over to Keller on the driver's side. Right?"

"Yeah. That's what happened."

"You're sure the pistol was a thirty-two automatic, aren't you Bill?"

"Yeah, I'm sure. I seen that gun plenty of times."

"Okay, then what did you say you did?"

"Well, like I said. He fell like a ton of bricks. Right about here on the ground."

"Then what?"

"I got one leg and Danny got the other and we dragged him over them big logs and threw him down over the bank. Right about over there."

"He was found at the base of a big tree a lot further down the hill," Callo said.

"Yeah. We dragged him down there. That's when Danny shot him again. Right in the side of the head."

They all walked down the embankment and ended up near the big tree where the remains were found four years ago.

Suddenly Dalton said, "I really don't know about this."

"What do you mean?"

"I don't know if I want to say anymore about this, man."

"Well, let me tell you what I really don't know about, Bill," Callo said. "I don't know about this bullshit story you just told us. But, let me tell you what I do know about."

McBride was caught off guard as much as Dalton was. He had no idea what Callo was up to.

"I do know that this murder could not have

happened the way you said it did. I also know that you were here with Danny when the body was found. You were not only here, you helped him take pictures and draw a diagram. Didn't you?"

"Yeah. I was here then, but..."

Callo cut him off. "I also know that you and Danny had a falling out, and you were real mad at him because he wouldn't help you get out of that trouble in Knox County."

"Yeah, but..."

Callo cut him off again. "You see this photograph? You see that black stuff there on the ground in this picture? Well, that's Keller's hair. The hair falls off first when a body starts to decompose. You see this right here, next to the hair? You see what I'm pointing to?"

"Yeah. I see it."

"That's Keller's sun glasses. Right there next to the hair. Now maybe I'm not to smart so I'm gonna ask you. Why would Keller have been wearing sunglasses if this happened in the middle of the night like you said it did?"

Dalton looked carefully at the photograph, but didn't say a word. McBride was quiet as well.

"Something else maybe you could tell me because maybe I'm not too smart. After Danny shot this guy and you both dragged his body across the ground, over those logs, and threw him down that ridge, and then dragged his body down to this tree. That is what you told us, isn't it?"

"Yeah. that's what I said."

"Well, then, you tell me how the Hell those

213

sun glasses could possibly have stayed on his face. Or even made it down here with the body."

"I don't know about no sun glasses, Callo."

"Well, here's the picture. Right there are the glasses. You and Danny took this picture when the remains were found. Didn't you?"

"I don't remember that," Dalton said.

"Bullshit! I'll tell you something else you don't know. Yesterday, me and a deputy came to this very spot. Right here where you are standing. We had a metal detector. You know what we found? We found a thirty-two caliber brass shell casing. Just like the one you all found right here in this same place four years ago when the remains were found. And not only that. We drove it to the lab in Nashville and they compared it to the one you all found. They told me they were both fired from the same gun. You know what that means?"

He knew but he couldn't say a word. He knew Callo had him right where he wanted him. McBride knew it too.

"Keller was shot with an automatic. That's a pistol that ejects the casing each time it's fired. But you know that. Don't you, Bill? We know he was shot twice in the head. But if we found both shell casings here at the base of this tree, then that means he wasn't shot once in the parking area and once here like you said. It means he was shot twice right here at this tree. Don't you think I'm right, Bill?"

"I guess so," Dalton said with his head hung.

"That means your story is nothing but

214

bullshit. Don't you think I'm right about that too, Bill?"

Dalton didn't answer. Callo's face was getting red. He was angry. He knew Dalton was lying and he knew he wasn't leaving without getting the truth out of him.

Callo reached into his pocket and pulled out the little white gift box. "Just so you don't think I'm bullshittin' you, Bill. Here are the two shell casings. The darker on is the one we found yesterday. Now, I'm going to tell you something, and I want you to pay real close attention." Dalton had his head hung down, staring at the ground like a statute.

"Look at me, God damnit!" Callo screamed. He didn't see him, but McBride even jumped. "I want you to look me in the eyes so I can see that you understand what I'm about to say. Because of you and this bullshit thing with Danny Bonet, I had to let three killers out of jail. And there's a seventeen year old girl whose life is now in danger." Callo could see that he either struck a nerve or scared the Hell out of him, because he could see a change in Dalton's expression.

"The only thing you accomplished by making up this story is that you left yourself open to a perjury charge because that statement you gave to McBride was a sworn statement. If anything happens to my witness, I'm going to see that you have more trouble than you've ever had in your whole life. Do you understand me?"

Dalton knew that Callo was serious and that

215

he had him between a rock and a hard place.

"Now if you don't start telling the truth, I'm going to start by sticking you with a perjury charge, and we'll just go from there."

Callo was sharp enough to know he had to leave Dalton a way out. If he boxed him in too tight, he might never admit his story was a lie

"Bill, if you admit you made a mistake and I'm sure you can come up with a reason, then I'll cut you loose and you'll never hear from me again," Callo said.

McBride finally got a clue and said," "Bill, weren't you doing a lot of coke about the time things went bad with you and Danny?"

"Yeah. I was doin' a Hell of a lot of coke back then."

"Well, is it possible you just imagined all this because of your feelings toward Danny and being all screwed up on coke at the same time?" McBride asked. "Because I'm telling you right now Bill, with everything Lieutenant Callo has, nobody is going to believe the statement you gave me under oath."

"Mark's right," Callo said.

"You gonna keep your word that you won't charge me with nothing ?"

"You've known me a long time. You know I'm a man of my word."

"Yeah, I know you are. Okay, I'll tell you this. I was real mad at Danny for the way he done me. I made up this story just to see him squirm a little. Like I did when he wouldn't help me out of jail in Knox County. I never would have let him take a murder rap though. Shit, when I gave McBride that statement, I didn't have no idea it would screw up a case you were working on Jake. And I sure don't want to get that girl hurt. You know me better than that." Dalton was almost in tears.

"Well, I thought I did. But that damn cocaine got your head all screwed up."

"Yeah. You're right there. But I ain't done no coke for a long time."

"Okay, I'll tell you what I'm going to do. Go up and wait by the car. I want to talk to Mark for a minute. Then he's going to take another statement from you. Only this time it's going to be the truth. Right?"

"It will be. I swear to you."

"Good, then we can all get the Hell out of here. This place gives me the creeps," Callo said.

Suddenly he felt sorry for Dalton. Maybe it was because he knew he never had a friend in his whole life. Callo patted him on the shoulder and asked him to go on up the hill.

"Mark, would you care to take another statement from him? You know, make sure he rescinds all this bullshit. He can use any reason he wants to. I don't care if he says it's because he was using drugs or the man in the moon made him say it. Just as long as he says he lied about Danny killing Keller. Then we're going to get to a phone and call the D.A. I'm going to ask him to call another session of the grand jury. I really need to get the

217

Hooks brothers back in jail before they get to Dawn Anderson."

"Sure. Whatever I can do to help. You know I really feel bad about all this."

"It's not your fault. I guess I should have talked to Jim myself before I took those warrants. And I think he played a little politics with the sheriff on it too."

"Yeah, I'd say you're right."

"Would you do me a favor and tell him that you're convinced that I need to go back to the grand jury with the Hooks brothers? He puts a lot of stock in something that comes from a T.B.I. agent." Callo thought to himself that was the least he could do since he came on like a big shot and almost screwed up the whole case.

"Yeah, sure. I'll tell him."

While McBride was taking a new statement from Dalton, Callo sat in his car. He never felt more relieved. He knew the sheriff would feel that way too. He was sure if he got another shot with the grand jury, he would get indictments against the Hooks brothers.

He called the dispatcher on his radio and told her to advise the sheriff that he would be in within the hour and needed to talk to him.

They all stopped at a phone booth in River City. Reynolds was in his office.

"Jim, this is McBride. I've got something urgent to talk to you about."

"I've got to leave my office in a few minutes. Can it wait until Monday?"

"No sir, this can't wait. I've been out here where Keller got killed with Callo and Dalton."

McBride cleared his throat and continued. "Jim, it seems Callo was right. Dalton has admitted he made up the whole thing about Danny Bonet."

"What do you mean he made it up?"

"It's like this. A while back Dalton got into some trouble in Knox County and wanted Bonet to help him out of it"

"Yes. I think I remember that. It screwed up a lot of drug cases in fact. But what's that got to do with this case?"

"Bonet wouldn't help him and Bill got all pissed off at him. Anyway Bill has admitted he made up this story to get even with him for not helping him. I've taken another sworn statement telling it all."

Reynolds was rarely at a loss for words, but these developments really caught him off guard. There was a long silence on the phone.

"Callo wants to talk to you for a minute if that's okay."

"Yes, I'll talk to him."

"Hey, Jim. I think we've hit the jackpot," Callo said. He knew he couldn't say what he really wanted to. He forced himself to be diplomatic with Reynolds.

"It sounds like you might have done just that. What do you suggest we do now?"

"I think I need to go before the grand jury again. As soon as possible. I'd like the chance to present my case against the Hooks brothers before something happens to my witness Dawn Anderson."

"How soon would you like to go?"

"I'd go today if you could arrange it."

"How about tomorrow?"

"That's fine with me."

"As far as I know they have never had a session on Saturday, but there's nothing saying they can't. I'll call the judge and clear it with him and then I'll call the jury foreman. I'll call you back in a few minutes."

"I won't be back in the office for about a half hour. Just give me enough time to get back and call the dispatcher. She'll find me."

Callo knew exactly where he would be. He'd be in with the sheriff letting him know what's going on.

Branson jumped him as soon as he hit the door. "Where the Hell have you been, Jake?" Branson was angry. "The press has been all over me. They want to know how the Hell we could have arrested the wrong people for murder. They want some answers, and quite frankly so do I."

"Calm down Sheriff. I've been out solving the Keller case. Again," Callo said with a smile.

Branson sensed Callo's uplifted mood and began to relax a little as he sat back down behind his desk.

"Well, how about letting me in on it. I am the sheriff, you know."

"Yeah, I know, Sheriff. I'm sorry for not keeping in touch, but I've been so busy I just couldn't take the time. I didn't want to get tangled up with the press either. I had more important things to do," Callo explained. "But I do have some good news."

"I sure hope so. I could use some right now."

"Then listen to this. I've been out at the murder scene with McBride and Dalton. Well, wait a minute, let me back up. I went out there yesterday morning and while I was there I realized if Keller was shot twice near the trees in the woods, and not once at the pull-off area and once down by the trees, like Dalton said in his statement, then there should be another shell casing near the tree."

"Okay, go on," Branson said.

"Anyway, I got with Wilder and we went out there with a metal detector he borrowed from his friend, and sure enough we found the second shell casing. Right there at the base of the tree. I don't know why they didn't find it years ago."

"I've seen the crime scene photographs and it's a wonder they even found the first one with all those people stomping around all over the place," Branson said.

"Anyway, We drove to the lab in Nashville and had it compared to the one they found four years ago. They told me it was fired from the same gun as the first one was."

"That's great."

"Yeah. But I still needed to get a shot at Dalton so I had McBride bring him out there. I had him walk through the whole thing like he said it happened. Then I hit him with the bombshell. I

221

showed him and that stupid ass McBride that there was no way it could have happened like he said."

"That's right."

"To make a long story short, he finally admitted he made up this bullshit story about Danny to get back at him. McBride took another statement telling how he lied about Danny."

"That's really terrific, Jake."

"It gets better. We called the D.A. and he's making arrangements to have the grand jury meet in a special session tomorrow."

"Tomorrow's Saturday?"

"I know. But that's what he said he was going to do."

"I'm glad he's come around. But I'll tell you one thing. He sure did make me look bad."

"Maybe now it will come back on him," Callo said. "But listen, Sheriff. He's doing the right thing now and we need him to prosecute this case, so let's not piss him off again."

"You're the one who pissed him off in the first place, Jake."

"Yeah, I know. Well, maybe we can work things out now."

"I hope so."

"If all goes well we should be able to arrest these guys again early tomorrow."

"That's good work," Branson said sincerely. I'll stay away from Reynolds and let you two work it out. I think that would be best for now."

"Yeah, I'd hate to see you get into it with him and screw things up again," Callo said. They both started laughing.

"I've got to tell you, I've been in some tight spots in the past but I really didn't know what I was going to do with this situation," Branson said.

He knew the fallout from the feud with the district attorney, arresting the wrong people, and having the case still unresolved would have been a disaster for his administration. Not to mention the law suit that would have followed.

"You didn't think for a minute that I'd leave you hanging on this one. Did you, Sheriff?"

"No. Not really because if I was hanging, so were you." They both started laughing again.

Chapter 15

One Down, Three to Go

Callo was up bright and early the next morning. The District Attorney kept his word and made arrangements for the grand jury to meet in special session. Agent McBride was going to meet Callo at the courthouse at eight o'clock.

On the way to the office he was thinking to himself how stupid McBride was going to look in front of the jury. After all, just a few days ago he was before the same panel telling them how convinced he was that Danny Bonet was a cold-blooded killer.

All the testimony lasted less than an hour. Callo was short and to the point. He was confident when the vote was taken the jury would hand down sealed indictments on the Hooks brothers for first degree murder. He knew, for certain when the jury foreman came out of the courtroom and called the Criminal Court Judge to come to the courthouse.

He was right. By ten-thirty that morning he was handed the papers authorizing the arrests.

Callo was walking to the elevator when he was approached by a reporter from the local newspaper. Apparently the reporter noticed the unusual activity at the courthouse for a Saturday morning and wanted to find out what was going on.

"Hey, Lieutenant. What's going on this morning? I noticed a couple of members of the Grand Jury leaving the courthouse."

"Well, buddy. Why don't you just hide and watch. You might get a scoop," Callo said with a great big grin on his face.

"Is it something on the Keller case? Did they indict anybody?" He kept probing as he got to the elevator with Callo.

"Listen, you know I can't make a comment on anything right now. Just stay close and it will be worth your time is all I can tell you. Okay?"

"Can you make a comment on arresting the wrong people the other day?"

"Yeah. The wrong people were not arrested the other day. The timing was off a little bit. That's all."

"Does that mean you're going to arrest them again? Is that why the grand jury met today?"

"You know. I have to wonder just what part of no comment you didn't understand. Just stick around. That's all I can tell you." Callo was relieved to be able to get away from the reporter. He didn't like their persistence.

"We got it, Sheriff," Callo said as he took the papers out of his pocket.

"That didn't take long at all, Jake."

"You know what took even less time?"

"What's that?" Branson asked.

"McBride getting out of the courthouse," Callo said. They both started laughing. "I kinda felt sorry for the dumb bastard. He must have looked like a real horses ass in there."

"Well, how do you want to make the arrests?" the sheriff asked.

"I think we should get a couple of deputies, go down to River City, and start at their house. They won't be expecting us. Hell, Eddie's probably busy on the phone with a lawyer trying to figure out how he's gonna sue me," Callo said.

"Oh, by the way. The press is already starting to poke around. Are you going to work up a press release?" Callo asked.

"Yes. In fact I started on it this morning when I came in. See how much confidence I have in you."

"Yeah, right. You could have fooled me a couple of days ago," Callo laughed.

"Get whoever you need and see if you can pick these guys up. I'm going to stay at the office and make some calls. Just stay in touch and let me know how you make out."

"Okay."

"Do you think you'll have any trouble?"

"No. If one of them gets hinky, I'll just shoot the son-of-a-bitch."

Callo arranged for several of the patrol officers and one of the other detectives to meet him at the jail. They had a short meeting in his office and headed for River City. The plan again called for hitting the house fast, even though it was the middle of the day. When they arrived, two officers went to the rear of the house. Callo and the others went to the wide open front door. Eddie and Jimmy were sitting on the couch drinking a beer and were quickly taken into custody. A search of the house failed to turn up Darrell.

Eddie was the only one to speak; as usual. "This is gettin' old. Don't you think?"

"Don't worry. It will never happen again because you're going to spend the rest of your life in the pen," Callo said with a great deal of satisfaction.

"Well, I ain't got nothing more to say, except I hate your guts Callo."

"You know what I think Eddie? I think you're just sore because you didn't get a chance to sue my ass off," Callo said as he was putting him in the back seat of a patrol car

"Fuck you. You gotta prove I did it first."

"Oh, I don't think that will be a problem. Anyway, I thought you weren't going to say anything else." He was mumbling something as Callo slammed the door in his face.

When Eddie and Jimmy were loaded and on their way to the jail, Callo went back into the house and asked Eagle Eye where Darrell was. His reply was a shrug of his shoulders.

When Callo picked up the phone to call the sheriff's office, Eagle Eye said, "Hey, buddy, I never said you could use the phone."

Callo looked him right in the eye, the good eye, and said, "That's because I didn't ask you. In the first place, I ain't your buddy. And in the second place, you better sit down and shut up while I make this call or I'm going to charge you with interfering with a felony arrest." Eagle Eye grumbled something under his breath and went to the kitchen for another beer.

"This is Callo. Tell the Sheriff we've got Eddie and Jimmy in custody. Ask him to make a press release to TV. and radio for Darrell Hooks. You know, wanted for first degree murder and anyone having information as to his whereabouts, please call the sheriff's office. He can get his description and a photo from the jail."

"I sure will," the dispatcher said.

"And tell him I'll be back in about an hour. I'm going to check a couple of places here in River City."

When he hung up the phone and was walking out the door, he turned to Eagle Eye and said, "The fact is, Mr. Hooks, you really ought to be thanking me for getting Eddie out of this house. Now maybe your family can have some peace."

Callo just got back into his car after checking a bar and pool hall when the dispatcher radioed him.

"Lieutenant, can you get to a phone and call

229

me right away? It's urgent."

"Ten four. Give me a few minutes to find one that's not tore up."

"Jake, I received a call from a nurse at the Oak Ridge Hospital a few minutes ago. She said she heard we were looking for Darrell Hooks on the radio and told me he is right now at the emergency room there."

"That's great. Did she say what he was being treated for?"

"Yeah, She said he has some kind of breathing problem, and goes there quite often. That's how she knew him."

"Okay, call Oak Ridge P.D. and have them send a car over there. I'm on my way from River City."

"Will do."

When Callo arrived at the hospital an Oak Ridge officer already had Hooks in custody. He was transferred to Callo's car and transported to the jail.

Darrell began to talk. He told Callo he knew there was something wrong, and they never should have been let out of jail. He also told him he knew they were going to be arrested again because he knew what the truth was. And he knew Callo would prove it.

When he arrived at the jail, there were several newspaper photographers on the sidewalk.

"See there, Darrell. You're a celebrity," Callo said. Darrell didn't reply.

Callo ran into the sheriff at the booking area

when he brought Darrell up to the jail.

"I gotta tell you, I feel good about things."

"So do I. So do I."

"Why don't you go home? Take a couple of days off. I know how much time you've put in lately," Branson said.

"Yeah, I just might do that. It would be nice to spend some time with my kids for a change," Callo said. "But there's something I need to take care of first."

He didn't elaborate. He just slipped away and went to his office to make a phone call.

"Danny? It's Callo."

"Hey, Jake. What's up?"

"Oh, same old thing. The reason I called is I need you to do me a big favor."

"If I can. Whatta ya need?" Bonet asked.

"Well, I need you to come down to my office right away."

"Come down there. For what?"

"I don't want to say over the phone. Just come in downstairs and see me. It's important to me or I wouldn't ask," Callo said.

"Tell me this. Should I bring my lawyer?"

"Be serious. Will you? I really need to see you right away. Trust me."

Danny Bonet sensed that Callo was almost pleading with him, so even though he felt uncomfortable going there because of all that went on with him, he agreed to meet Callo in his office. "I'll be there in about fifteen minutes Jake."

"Thanks. I'll be waiting for you."

When Bonet arrived he found Callo alone in the detectives office. "Well, here I am. Now what the Hell is so important?"

"I want to tell you something. Then I want you to do me a favor," Callo said.

"Okay."

"I made arrests in the Keller case again a while ago. I went to the grand jury this morning and got the indictments and we rounded them all back up again."

"That's great. You said you would get it all worked out."

"Yeah, I got with McBride and your buddy Dalton. Man, I really took him apart. It wasn't too hard to prove he was a liar. He admitted it. McBride took a new statement from him and he told how he just said those things to get back at you. But, he did say he never would have let you take a murder rap." Callo laughed.

"That was real big of him."

"I knew years ago that Eddie was the trigger man," Danny said. "I hope you got a tight case."

"Shit. When I arrested them the other day I got confessions out of two of them. I don't think we'll have any trouble making it stick."

"That's great. What do you want me to do? Sounds to me like you got it all wrapped up."

"I know how hard you worked on this case. And I know you knew who did it, but things just didn't work out back then."

"Yeah, well shit happens. What can I say? The important thing is that you got the job done."

"Anyway, while I was going through the case file you had on it, I ran across your notes about you making the notification to Mrs. Keller."

"Yeah, that was a pretty hard thing to do," Bonet said.

"It must have been, because I found those very words in the file that you wrote in pencil. You remember making that note?"

"Yeah, I remember that."

"Well, I'd like you to do me a favor right now. I'd like you to be the person that makes the call to Mrs. Keller and tell her that the people that killed her son have been arrested."

Callo picked up the phone, dialed the number, and handed the phone to Danny.

"Hello. Is this Mrs. Keller?" Bonet cleared his throat just as he did almost five years ago when he called to tell her that her son's skeletal remains had been found.

"Yes, it is."

"Ma'am, this is Danny Bonet. I was the detective working on the case of your son's murder. Do you remember me?"

"Yes. I remember you, Mr. Bonet. What is it I can do for you, sir?"

"Well, Ma'am, I'm calling for Lieutenant Callo at the sheriff's office. He wanted me to inform you that he has arrested three people for the murder of your son."

"Oh, my. I never expected this. It's been such a long time. Three people were arrested for killing Jack, you say." Mrs. Keller was clearly repeating his words for the benefit of her husband who must have been in the same room. "And when did this happen? The arrests I mean," she said with her voice cracking with emotion.

"Just a little while ago, Ma'am. I'm sorry I can't give you much detail right now. Mr. Callo will call you in a day or so and give you more information," Danny said. "We thought you would like to know about this right away, so that's why we're calling."

"Thank you for calling. I must say I never thought anything would come of the investigation. What with that crooked sheriff you had there and all."

"Yes, Ma'am. I know what you mean." Danny smiled. "But I assure you it's true. Detective Callo worked very hard in this case and he would never quit."

"And you say there were three of them?" she asked again.

"Yes Ma'am. They were all brothers."

"Well, I just don't know what to say."

"Mrs. Keller, Callo will call you soon and give you more details. He'll be in touch soon. Okay?"

"Thank you again for calling. I must tell you without knowing all there is to know, I'm so relieved. I've got to call my sister and tell her the news. Thank you again."

"Yes Ma'am. You're welcome. Goodbye."

Callo looked across the desk at Danny as he hung up the phone. He was sure he could see tears in Danny's eyes. He didn't say a word. He just grinned.

"Thanks. I really appreciate that," Danny said sincerely.

"I thought that was the least I could do. I'm glad you came down."

"Me too."

Bonet stayed for about an hour and Callo filled him in on the breaks he got in the case, and how he took Dalton back to the scene and caught him in all those lies. When Danny left, Callo went back up to the sheriff's office.

"Where the Hell have you been, Jake? The press wants to talk to you," Branson said.

"I had to take care of something. Mr. and Mrs. Keller needed to know that we solved the case," Callo said.

"Oh good. I'm glad you took care of that."

Callo felt good, not only because he solved a very difficult case, and was able to overcome all the obstacles in his way, but also because he had the chance to do something nice for Danny Bonet. He felt good too because there would be an ending to this saga for the Kellers that was long overdue.

Anthony Callo spent the next few months taking some time off, catching up on some other cases he left pending, and making sure the Keller case was ready for trial. He worked closely with the District Attorney's office and appeared at all the pre-trial motion hearings in the case. He had developed a good relationship with the D.A.'s staff, including Jim Reynolds. He learned to respect their needs for the proper prosecution of a case. Murder is a serious crime and had to be handled right.

He told the sheriff he didn't want to start on the next unsolved murder case until this one was completely finished. That meant after the trial, and what a trial it was. Darrell and Jimmy declined a deal that their attorneys pleaded with them to take. If they had testified against Eddie, they would have been out in two years. The intimidation factor from Eddie was so strong, they decided to take their chances.

Each one of the defendants had his own court appointed lawyer. This made being a witness very difficult. First the prosecutor examined them, then each one of the attorneys did their cross examination.

Then there was re-direct and re-cross. The trial only lasted five days, but to Callo when he was on the stand, it seemed to be lasting months.

It was an experience to watch Doctor Bass as he testified. He seemed to amaze the jury with how he made positive identification of the skeletal remains.

The star witness turned out to be Dawn Anderson. She testified about how she became involved with Eddie Hooks as a very young girl and how the murder took place.

She also stressed the fact that Eddie made it clear to her that she would end up the same way Jack Keller did if she ever told on him. Her quiet demeanor and country charm on the witness stand made her a very credible witness. The defense attorneys tried their best to shake her, but they could not.

The whole Danny Bonet and Bill Dalton mess was never brought up in court. As hard pressed for defense evidence as the attorneys were, none of them wanted anything to do with Bill Dalton.

About a year later Bill Dalton survived an almost point blank range shotgun blast to his chest. The only person he would tell the name of his assailant to was Anthony Callo, but only on the condition that he would never bring a charge or reveal the name. Six months later Dalton was stabbed to death during an argument with a long time rival in the parking lot of a convenient store.

The state did not seek the death penalty in the Keller case. Life without parole was good enough for them if they got a conviction.

When all was said and done, the jury only deliberated for five hours. Mr. and Mrs. Keller sat quietly on the first row, as they did throughout the entire trial when the jury announced they had reached a verdict.

The verdict for each of the defendants was the same: guilty of first degree murder.

Callo looked over at Jimmy and Darrell as the verdict was read. Each one hung his head and must have been thinking to themselves what fools they were not to have taken the state's deal.

Callo was standing in the hallway when the deputies brought them out. Eddie was livid. "You know you framed me, Callo. I'm gonna make you pay for doing this to me," he yelled. Callo just shook his head in disgust.

Mr. and Mrs. Keller came over to Callo and shook his hand, thanking him for his hard work.

He also looked at Eddie's younger brothers and sisters and wondered to himself if now maybe they would have a chance, or if any of them would grow up and follow the example set for them by their older brothers.

When almost everyone had cleared the hallway, Sheriff Branson came up to Callo and introduced him to Don Golden.

"Jake, Don is the husband of Anne Golden who was killed in 1981 near the river."

"Yes sir, Sheriff. I'm familiar with the case."

"I told Don that you would be starting on that case soon, and I wanted him to meet you," Branson said.

Callo shook his hand. "Don, glad to meet you. Is right now soon enough? Let's go down to my office and talk about it for a while, if you have time."

"That would be great. I've waited too many years for something to finally happen with my wife's murder, to not have time now," Don said. "I'll tell you something else."

"What's that?"

"I just know that you're going to solve it too."

"Thanks for the vote of confidence. But the only promise I can make you is that I'll give it my best shot and try to make it come out like this one."

"That's all I can ask for. I'm sure you will."

As Don and Callo were walking to the elevator, and the sheriff was walking to his office, he turned and said, "Hey, Jake. That's one down, and three to go."